A-Z Advancing Geography:
Fieldwork

DAVE HOLMES AND
DAVE FARBROTHER

Geographical
Association

FSC
BRINGING
ENVIRONMENTAL
UNDERSTANDING TO ALL

Acknowledgements

The authors would like to thank Sue Warn for her helpful advice on this book, and in particular for permission to use material from her **Fieldwork Investigation** series. Janet Keeble for her technical input and role as the 'thought police' and John Wragg for his artistic input.

The Geographical Association would like to thank the people who supplied photographs, especially, Professor Tim Burt, Steve Day, Robert Grandfield, John Hope-Hislop, Bob Jones, Tony Jones, John Reader and Paula Richardson.
The GA is also grateful to the Ordnance Survey for permission to reproduce OS mapping, and to © Munch Museum/Munch - Ellingsen Group, BONO, Oslo, DACS, London 2002, for *The Scream* (page 6), 1893 (oil, tempera and pastel on board) by Edvard Munch (1863-1944). Image supplied by Nasjonalgalleriet, Oslo/Bridgeman Art Library, London.

The Authors

Dave Farbrother is a Lecturer in Geology at Shrewsbury Sixth Form College and is currently the Shropshire County U19 Football Manager.

Dave Holmes lectures part-time at King Edward's Sixth Form College, Stourbridge. He also works as Geography Advisor to the FSC.

ISBN 1 899085 79 3
First published 2000. Reprinted with amends 2002.
Impression number   10 9 8 7 6 5 4 3 2
Year   2003   2002

Published by the Geographical Association,
160 Solly Street, Sheffield S1 4BF.
The Geographical Association is a registered charity: no 313129.

The Publications Officer of the GA would be happy to hear from other potential authors who have ideas for geography books. You may contact the Officer via the GA at the address above.

Copy edited by Rose Pipes
Designed by Ledgard Jepson Ltd.
Cartography by Paul Coles
Printed and bound in China through Colorcraft Ltd., Hong Kong

Contents

Introduction

The aim of this book is to help you sleep at night. The authors have experienced the pitfalls that lurk beneath the surface of many fieldwork projects, and have themselves negotiated the bumpy terrain between an idea and its successful execution, and we hope what we learnt will work for you too. The book is essentially a fieldwork manual for AS and A2 geography students, and will furnish you with the skills and techniques you need to tackle the personal investigation element of your coursework with confidence. If it also manages to turn you into enthusiastic and enquiring geographers, deepen your understanding of the subject, and help you become more effective decision-makers and problem-solvers, then we authors will sleep at night as well!

Using this book

This fieldwork guide is more of a manual than a textbook. It is written in the form of an alphabetical directory of the more achievable and relevant field techniques, together with more general project advice. The 30 units vary in length between 2, 4 and 6 pages, with more space being given to 'core **specification**' themes such as rivers, coasts, urban and rural. All the units carry a short introduction, and most of them include the following:

- Suggestions about when/where and how to use the technique
- Comments about the limitations of the technique
- General hints and tips
- An idea of how long a particular field technique may take
- A list of the equipment required
- Suggested uses of information and communications technology
- References to useful articles and books

There is inevitably a variation in the pitch and demands of these 30 themes, though there is not a progression of difficulty from A through to Z. Thus, Photographing may be classed as easy, while Discovery Fieldwork is more demanding. Only you, the user, can judge which ones are most appropriate for your circumstances and skills.

It is assumed that you will move around between units and look at links between them, making full use of the cross-references, the Index, the suggested external references and the Appendix, as necessary. Where specialist words are used, they appear in bold type and are defined in the Glossary on pages 108-110.

The authors recognise that many of the proposed field surveys will pose difficulties for you, particularly where members of the public are involved. Being an observer/recorder may make you feel awkward and self-conscious, so think about working in pairs or groups. Remember to stay focused on your task, and always put safety first, making sure that people know where you are and what you are doing - read the section on Fieldwork Safety on page 9 before you embark on any of the projects suggested.

How to get started

There is an immense variety in geography, and herein lies its appeal. It has something for everyone, from the gravedigger to the town planner. So use whatever interests you have as a springboard into your coursework. Start by gathering information that is easily and freely available:

1. Refer to Project Planning on pages 6-8, visit the X-Files and Yawn Projects, and cast your eye over the list of Suggested Project Titles, pages 10-13.

2. Check the syllabus/specification details from your teacher, or download them from the Internet (refer to the Specification **matrix** in the Appendix on page 103). These include comments and advice on what the Examiners are looking for, and the way in which the projects will be marked (see also Figure 1)

3. Use your wits to get further starting ideas - look at your GCSE project(s) or earlier school work, see if there are past projects that you can study (particularly if they have been graded).

4. Consider your own personal strengths and skills. Stand back and take a long hard look at yourself:

- Are you handy at art and sketching?
- Are you confident when dealing with adults?
- Can you handle 'funny' looks whilst doing surveys?
- Do you care about other people's problems and feelings?
- Are you prepared to research background information?

- Do you prefer working in a group or by yourself?
- What aspects of geography appeal to you?
- Do you like practical fieldwork?
- What are you like at statistics?
- Do you lack self-discipline?

Having addressed these and other questions you are in a better position to judge what types of project you are best suited to undertaking. Aim to tailor your project to make best use of your strengths and to avoid exposing your weaknesses.

Ways of working

The current thinking is that geographical fieldwork should generally be undertaken by groups comprising no more than 10-12 students. The group members should all contribute something specific to the project and the overall theme should be defined as a single broad idea or question (as suggested in the Rural Enquiries unit on pages 70-73). However, while all members of the group share a common pool of primary and secondary data, each individual must devise and pursue their own specific route to enquiry, with its own title or hypothesis. The completed project/report must bear the hallmark of the individual, particularly in terms of presentation, analysis and evaluation. In other words, you must be sure that your work is individual and distinctive from that of others in the group.

This 'multi-activity' approach can be adopted for several of the Suggested Project Titles on pages 10-13, for example, 'An analysis of stream channel characteristics to see how the nature of these **relationships** vary downstream'. This title can be unlocked and broken down into a number of tightly focused and relatively independent routes to enquiry:

- River discharge increases downstream but this may not be proportional to distance from source. *(statement form)*

- Is the ratio of channel width to depth approximately constant with progression downstream? *(question form)*
- Flow velocities are highest in the deepest sections of channels. *(hypothesis form)*

Some golden rules

Having settled upon a project title or question, consider the following list of questions:

1. Is it largely *geographical in essence*, involving the investigation of a **spatial** pattern, relationship or problem/issue?

2. Is it *manageable* in terms of scale, time, equipment and transport - most importantly is it local and sufficiently small in area (e.g. a few square kilometres only)?

3. Is it *achievable* in terms of a varied and accessible programme of primary and secondary data?

4. Is it *of interest to you*, and do you have a connection or personal involvement with it?

5. Will it *link with the course* you are studying, particularly the core units or themes, and with current national planning or political initiatives?

6. Does it give you the opportunity to demonstrate and evidence *your key skills* in some or all of the six main categories? (Refer to Key Skills, pages 46-47).

7. When the report is near completion, will it end up being within the *official word limit*, will its sections conform to the *required structure*, and will it be submitted by the *official deadline date*?

Does your study do these things? Tick

Consider change over space/time ☐
Check out a hypothesis ☐
Analyse **patterns/distributions** ☐
Identify geographical processes ☐
Test theories/models ☐
Examine local issues ☐
Study people's behaviour/perceptions ☐
Use and evaluate equipment ☐
Appreciate environmental impacts ☐
Suggest management solutions ☐
Search for secondary information ☐
Apply appropriate statistics ☐

The more items you can tick the better!

	Section	Words	% of marks	Comments	Action
1	INTRODUCTION - statement of purpose/aims and key questions/hypotheses. Setting the scene, e.g. annotated site map defining the terms in the title, delimiting the study area.	up to 400	10	Deliver the facts succinctly so that a 'stranger' will understand	
2	DATA COLLECTION - when, how and why the primary and secondary data were collected, including evidence and problems.	300	15	This section can be more or less delivered as a tabulation	
3	DATA REPRESENTATION - a 'healthy' range of visual techniques including cartographic, diagrammatic, graphic and photographic.	200	10	You can use ICT, but credit is given for hand drawn work	
4	DATA ANALYSIS - detailed description and explanation of the results, trends and messages implied by the data. Use of statistical techniques and models where appropriate.	1000 max	25	These two sections are the most heavily weighted - they amount to 50% of the marks, so don't sell them short. The Examiner will look here to judge how good or bad you are	
5	CONCLUSION - come to a decision on the key question/hypothesis, draw the threads together, and critically evaluate the validity of the exercise in terms of strengths and weaknesses. Set the project in a wider geographical context, if possible.	600	25		
6	COMMUNICATION - style of writing (including spelling, punctuation and grammar) and use of geographical terminology.		15	Projects exceeding the word limit can only gain 6 out of 15%	

Notes

- Only words in the text are counted, those used on diagrams (including annotation) are 'free'.
- Communication also involves the structuring of the report, the inclusion of titles, figure and page numbers, referencing of diagrams in the text, and the acknowledgement of data sources.
- Include a time schedule within the 'Action' column, and try to stick to it!

Figure 1: An example of guidance for coursework from the Edexcel B Specification (2500 words is the advised limit).

Project Planning

Planning your own coursework project is a rare opportunity to take control of one aspect of your educational life. This is a challenge: you'll need to be well organised, well motivated and comfortable with the idea of independent learning.

The ability to project plan is quite a sophisticated skill. Many of the problems that arise are fairly easy to predict; however, planning is not just about avoiding problems, it is also working out what the project needs, juggling these requirements with your other priorities and devising a strategy to make it happen (see Figure 1, particularly the text in green boxes). Fortunately, most Examiners were young themselves once and some of them can remember what it was like.

How to avoid pitfalls

1. Forward planning saves time and stress (yours and that of people close to you).

2. Check regularly that your project is not departing from the syllabus/**specification** criteria.

3. Make sure shared equipment will be available when you need it.

4. Conduct a **pilot survey** and a risk assessment and obtain permission to survey.

5. Maintain an appropriate balance between primary and secondary data.

6. Make sure your prime time for collecting data does not clash with your summer job and/or holiday.

So how does it really happen?

Your project may begin inside your head, with a bright idea or rough plan (sometimes completely out of the blue). More likely, it arises from conversations and experiences with others. Your project may also be suggested or 'lifted' from secondary sources such as television, radio, newspapers, the Internet, books, past students' work, or from your geographical studies.

Whatever its origin, permit the germ of the idea to bounce around your head for no more than a few days – don't let it go stale by sitting back and thinking you have cleared the biggest hurdle. In terms of geography coursework, your initial idea should adhere to the first four 'golden rules' in the 'Introduction' (page 5), though it may be too early for you to be sure of this. One of the advantages of operating as part of a group is that your early ideas will get initial guidance not only from your teacher but also from other students.

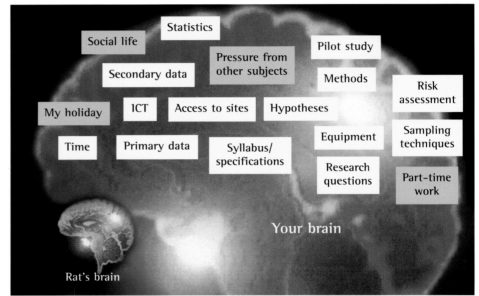

Figure 1: Your brain (with rat's brain for comparison).

Your basic idea could be: 'to investigate people's environment in urban areas'. First, convert this basic idea into an aim with a clear geographical dimension. For example: 'I intend to find out how environmental quality affects the lives of city/town dwellers, and their preferences about where to live'. Then turn this into a general question: 'Are there more environmental pressures and problems in present day urban life than most people realise?'

At this stage you may need to refine your basic idea to achieve a manageable project. In this example, you could identify and compare two quite different residential areas in a town/city, or focus down to particular elements such as traffic congestion, building decay, air pollution, quality of landscaping, etc.

Next, attack the general question with a barrage of key questions; these demand fairly straightforward answers and will help to 'unlock' the general question and allow you to identify the main elements of your project.

- *Where* is my study area(s)? Can I easily delimit it?

- *What* environmental elements will I focus on? What will I leave out?

- *Why* is environmental quality important to urban dwellers? (Or can you be content without it?)

- *How* am I going to collect convincing primary data?

- *Who* can I get to help, and what can I reasonably expect from them?

- *When* will the main data be collected, and what time frame (if any) will I use for the project title?

Now you should have a good handle on the scope of your project and be able to construct a project title. This should be a single sentence that is reasonably specific about place, time and objective. It could be one of the following:

'All gloss and no susbstance', *Geography Review*, vol. 10, no. 1, September 1996.

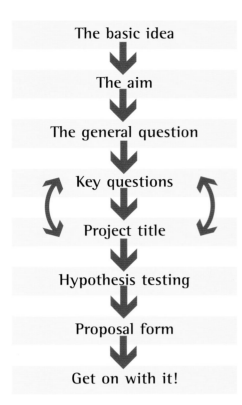

The basic idea

↓

The aim

↓

The general question

↓

Key questions

↕

Project title

↕

Hypothesis testing

↓

Proposal form

↓

Get on with it!

Figure 2: From the basic idea to the actual fieldwork.

1. *'Residential area X has a much higher quality of environment than area Y.'*
2. *'Does community Z underestimate the environmental pressures and problems affecting it?'*
3. *'In town T some environmental issues, such as traffic, are considered far more important than others, such as landscaping.'*

If your project title is not already in the form of a hypothesis (as in example number 1 above) it can be useful to express it as a hypothesis or research question which can be tested using the evidence from your data collection. In some physical projects it is possible to construct a null hypothesis which can then be tested statistically; for example: 'There is no significant relationship between tree girth and the distance to the nearest mature tree in woodland W.'

Finally, you will probably have to fill in a proposal form (or similar) to a set deadline. Proposal forms vary depending on the awarding body/examining board. They require you to outline your intended project in greater detail than the title, defining terms, delimiting the study area, and outlining a suggested programme of primary and secondary data gathering (see Figure 3). Your proposal form is sent to external examiners, whose views on the acceptability or otherwise of your project are returned on a duplicate form so that you can incorporate their advice into your work.

Time management

You will generally have 3-6 months to deliver your coursework project. This time will fly by all too quickly! Most awarding bodies reckon on 1-2 days fieldwork and about 30-50 hours for all the rest, including planning, researching, discussion, and writing up. This amounts to 1^1/2 weeks of solid work!

Notes

- Instead of being dragged out over several months, much to the exasperation of everyone involved, the whole process need take no more than a few days (Figure 2). You will need to discuss it with your teacher and the group you may be working with.

- Some of you will not need to go through the process (Figure 2) – you can bypass it by simply transforming the basic idea into a project title, and using the key questions to unlock it.

- Geography coursework projects can be very successful without using any form of hypothesis testing (see Urban topics in 'Suggested Project Titles', page 13).

- Once you start gathering data, you might want to modify your original title. This is perfectly acceptable as long as you state and justify this in your introduction.

Start by devising a schedule, as in the Action column on Figure 1 on page 5 of the Introduction. Allocate your time roughly in proportion to the percentage weightings of each section. For example, 3-5 hours and one side of word-processed A4 (plus an annotated base-map) should be enough for the introduction, which may be worth only 10%.

Don't go overboard on the data gathering, then find yourself lumbered with either too much data or too many words in the final report, or both.

Make sure you allocate sufficient time to write up data analysis and the conclusion/evaluation - two sections which together are worth about 50% of the total marks. And give yourself a few days' leeway before the deadline so you can come back to your written report, and make final additions/adjustments in terms of:
- the contents page
- page numbers
- cross-references
- the abstract (100-200 words summarising the report)
- appendices
- acknowledgement of sources
- late developed photographs
- the front cover (with official form, including word count and candidate number).

Let's say you are on an AS course, your fieldwork takes place in early November, and the internal completion date is early March. You have four months to deliver your finished report, a period which includes the Christmas holidays (a suspect time for academic work) and February half term. So an appropriate action plan might be as follows:

1. Introduction: draft version by mid-November

2. Data collection: including secondary researching, concluded by the end of November.

3. Data representation and analysis: developed and concluded during December and January.

4. Conclusion and Evaluation: draft version during early February.

5. Final checks and reviewing: during the February half-term.

A more detailed action plan is shown in Figure 4 overleaf.

Hints and tips
- Keep all project work together in a separate folder or file. Organise this into sections for easy retrieval prior to tutorials or group work.

- Consider using a dictaphone (memotaker) when discussing the progress of the project with your teacher, whose advice and guidance may be ignored because you cannot write it down quickly enough in an understandable form.

- Decide how you will present and analyse your data before you collect it. This applies particularly to questionnaire surveys and interviews, but also to less obvious approaches such as correlation statistics.

- 2500-4000 words is really not that many (this book has over 67 000 words in total). You can expect an average of about 600 words per side of A4 when it is word-processed using 12 point type. More problems arise from too many words, rather than too few: use your report-writing skills to edit work, cutting out repetition, 'padding' and irrelevant material. This should help you to produce a lean, streamlined and economical final version.

- Maintaining your motivation over 3-6 months is a real problem. Start early while you are fresh and enthusiastic, and keep the project ticking over. Check your action plan regularly – if your timings turn out to be unrealistic, adjust them, then stick to the revised plan.

'Carrying out an individual project', *Geography Review*, vol. 4, no. 3, January 1991.

Type of data	Source	
	Primary	Secondary
Qualitative	Field sketches/photographs	Historical photos, postcards, scanned photos, etc.
	Sketch maps	Ordnance Survey and street maps, brochures, etc.
	Interviews/questionnaires	Television/local radio, newspaper articles
	Quality surveys	Official site evaluations, e.g. Blue Flag Awards
	Site observation/note taking	Official/company literature and brochures
Quantitative	Traffic surveys	Other students, County Council, Highways Agency
	Population/employment surveys	Census data – Small Area Statistics, *Kelly's Directory*
	Microclimate investigations	Meterological Office
	Channel surveys	Data from field centres, e.g. Field Studies Council centres, and the Environment Agency
	Land use mapping	Ordnance Survey and land utilisation maps

Figure 3: Primary and secondary sources of qualitative and quantitative data.

ICT links

- Word-process your fieldwork report if you can: it looks better, you can do an automatic spell-check and word count, and you can edit and cut and paste text. This helps you save time as well as produce a punchy and well-presented piece of work.

- Use computer spreadsheets where appropriate, (e.g. Microsoft *Excel*), to process the data, particularly where large number sets are involved.

- Computer-generated graphs look good, but don't overdo them. You can use a variety of techniques to present your data, but it is the quality of analysis that really counts. Use **annotation** as much as possible.

- Scanned images can greatly enhance your project, but always acknowledge their source. Digital photos can be manipulated to maximise their effect and the available space.

- Use the Internet to tap into a vast source of information (but beware the time and expense involved!). This is essentially secondary data but if sorted, refined and manipulated it can be considered primary in nature (though it would be unwise to use data derived in this way as a major source).

Stage	Activity	How long?	Completion	Quality
1	From basic idea to completed proposal form	2 days	Early November	✓
2	Write draft Introduction			
3	Draw annotated base-map			
4	Wrap-up basic primary fieldwork			
5	Questionnaire survey (if appropriate)			
6	Photographs, sketches, scanned images			
7	Researching/collecting secondary data (local studies library)			
8	Process the collected data			
9	Present some of the data as diagrams, etc.			
10	Discussion/analysis of data collected			
11	Write up draft conclusion/evaluation			
12	Final edit and word process			

Notes The 'How long' and 'Completion' columns are blank since each project will vary. A neat touch is to evaluate your work for tutorial sessions, i.e. double tick = grade 'A', single tick = 'B/C', question mark = 'D/E' and cross = 'U' (place these in the Quality column).

Figure 4: Example action plan.

Final checklist

- ☐ Base maps prepared for use in the field.

- ☐ Recording sheets prepared and plenty of copies made in case you spoil some.

- ☐ Interviews set up well in advance and letters written to the relevant people.

- ☐ Questionnaires piloted, modified (where necessary) and checked by teacher/supervisor.

- ☐ Sample size worked out to ensure representative sample, which also minimises bias.

- ☐ Sources for background material/secondary data researched, studied and recorded.

- ☐ Liaison with the rest of the fieldwork group (if appropriate) to identify roles, responsibilities, equipment sharing, potential difficulties, review sessions, etc.

And finally ...

Your study does not have to be original to get a high mark. It's almost impossible to come up with a truly original investigation: the ground is just too well trodden. When marking a study, an Examiner will check the proposal form, then probably turn to the final section. The quality of your conclusions and evaluations will determine their important first impression: it is here that they will differentiate between the good, the bad, the feeble, the thorough, the careless, the dull and the lazy ... So where do you stand?

Fieldwork Safety

Fieldwork is generally a very safe activity but all actions we undertake carry some element of danger or risk. Your job is to anticipate, minimise and manage any possible risks, starting at the planning stage and extending throughout the fieldwork. Use your common sense, be aware of your surroundings and follow the safety advice given below. Some of this will only be relevant in certain situations, but others will be applicable in all out-of-doors activities. The advice given below applies to most fieldwork situations; more detailed comments relating to specific sites can be found in the relevant units of this book. Whatever you are doing, you should carry out a 'Risk Assessment' (see pages 68-69). Safety remains your personal responsibility, though in many cases this is shared with other students and supervising staff.

Photo: Tim Burt.

Safety issue	Managing safety (yours, the public and the environment)	Relevant areas
Clothing (hypothermia)	Fieldwork is miserable if you are cold and wet. Wear appropriate warm clothing and take water-proofs, hat and gloves when necessary. Your footwear should be fit for purpose and comfortable.	All
Country Code	You must avoid fire, injury and stress to livestock and damage to yourselves, i.e. climbing loose stonewalls, crossing barbed-wire fences, avoiding bulls (see Appendix, page 103).	All countryside surveys
Drowning	When working at the coast, check tides and sea conditions. Crossing large rivers is very dangerous especially in flood. Immersion can induce hypothermia.	Coastal and river environments
Emergency kit	Try not to get lost (a map may help if you can use one). Make sure you know what to do in an emergency, i.e. where to summon help and what to do if you, or someone you are with gets injured. Consider taking a small first-aid kit, a torch and a whistle (and emergency food for remote areas).	All, excluding some urban environments
Herd mentality	Group work encourages a 'herd' mentality in which individual students switch-off from making their own decisions and lose awareness of the potential risks that surround them. It may also lead to anti-social behaviour, e.g. not considering other pedestrians on pavements.	All
Identification	It's always a good idea when dealing with the public to carry some form of personal identification as it makes other people feel safer with you, e.g. student card, laminated badge, letter from school/college.	All, especially questionnaire surveys
Medication	If you regularly take/have medication, then don't forget it when you go outside, e.g. Ventolin for asthmatic or an Epi-pen for people with severe allergies. Suntan lotion is also important when it is sunny.	All
Missing	Always tell a responsible adult where you are going and when you are expected back. Carry a public transport timetable if appropriate. If possible take a mobile phone, but don't rely on it to work everywhere, especially in remote locations.	All
Money	Always take some money with you (including change and/or a 'phonecard for the telephone). You may need it to get home in an emergency or to buy an ice-cream!	All
Paths and tracks	Never run down hills as things can go out of control very easily. Take care on steep paths and tread carefully on potentially slippery ground, especially wet grassy banks, boulders in rivers and on the foreshore.	Mountainous and rural locations
Permission	Make sure you obtain written permission to enter private property.	Anywhere private
Traffic	Be sensible, be aware of your surroundings and don't expect drivers to be aware of your presence, especially in quiet rural areas.	Towns and country lanes
Working alone	In most situations it is not advisable to work on your own. Bring a responsible friend or relative who could help or even a dog which can get help if things go wrong.	All, except some urban situations

Note: *If things do go badly wrong and you need to ring the emergency services they will ask you your name, which service you require (including Coastguard and Mountain Rescue) and for details of your location and the nature of the incident. Be prepared to supply information on all of these.*

Suggested Project Titles

We have trawled the known Universe to come up with the following menu of suggested project titles. They are categorised into:

    Black = question format
    Blue = statement format
    Green = (testable) hypothesis format.

This list is intended for those of you who, through no fault of your own, have hit a brick wall in terms of starting ideas. These suggested titles are not exhaustive – you can elaborate upon many by utilising your particular interests and abilities, local knowledge, or some personal advantage in terms of access to data. There is an inevitable degree of overlap between some of these titles and some are deliberately vague to allow you to make your own interpretation.

Photo: Frank Lane Picture Agency.

Each title is scored in the third and fourth columns as follows:

Third column: The likely scale of the project, i.e. S = a localised, small-scale undertaking, L = a spatially extensive enquiry. The coding M/L has been used depending upon the size of the area.

Fourth column: The level of difficulty or achievability of the project, from 1 to 4. A score of 1 suggests a straightforward and easily manageable enquiry; a score of 4 indicates a challenging undertaking.

Notes: The titles are numbered, but are listed in no particular order. Those with numbers in red tinted cells could easily take you down a non-geographical line of enquiry.

Environmental topics

No.	Suggested title	Likely scale	Level of achievability
1	An evaluation of the various environmental/social and economic changes resulting from a major construction at site Z.	S/M	4
2	To what extent do the resident's perception of flood threats match the reality of these events in town/area Y?	S/M	4
3	A study of the impact of afforestation/deforestation in area Z.	M	3
4	An investigation into footpath maintenance, usage and connectivity in area Z	S/M	2
5	There is a decay of noise proportional to distance away from a linear/point source of noise.	S	1
6	What is the pattern of atmospheric pollution around an industrial operation at site Z?	S	2
7	An environmental/energy audit of my school/college/home.	S	3
8	A study of the use and distribution of rock type Y (a local outcrop).	M/L	2
9	How vulnerable is the Green Belt around conurbation Z?	L	3
10	The industrial/agricultural activity at site X does not affect local water courses.	S	3
11	Are the pressures at conservation site(s) X effectively managed?	S/M	2
12	What might be the environmental and ecological impacts after the removal of a stretch of hedgerow?	S	2
13	A study of the various impacts of quarrying at W.	M	3

Transport topics

No.	Suggested title	Likely scale	Level of achievability
1	An investigation into the effectiveness of traffic calming measures in town X (or village Y).	S/M	2
2	Why do journey-to-work patterns vary between different urban wards or parishes?	M	2
3	A cost/benefit analysis of the traffic management options currently being considered for village Z.	S	3
4	An evaluation of public transport provision in rural area Y.	L	3
5	To what extent are the main roads and pavements of town X congested?	M	3
6	An enquiry into the effectiveness of Park and Ride schemes in town X.	M	2
7	A consideration of the efficiency of the transport networks in urban area X (or rural environment Y).	L	3
8	During peak times of the day, traffic reaches saturation at various points in town/village X.	S/M	1
9	A review of the nature, use and adequacy of car parking in town Z.	M/L	1
10	A survey of the environmental and economic impact of a new road scheme in town/area Y.	M/L	2
11	A study into the impact of the closure of a branch railway line on rural settlements in area X.	L	3
12	An investigation into the route quality of a main road through town X.	S/M	1
13	The case for and against re-opening the railway station at site Z.	S/M	3
14	What factors influence the daily and weekly traffic flows at major junctions in town X?	S/M	1
15	The impact of heavy goods vehicles (HGV's) on village Z.	S	2
16	An investigation into the issues surrounding usage of transport terminals, e.g. bus/rail stations, airports.	S	2

Physical topics

No.	Suggested title	Likely scale	Level of achievability
1	An analysis of stream channel characteristics in river X to discover how the nature of these relationships varies downstream.	S/M	2
2	What factors influence flow velocities in river channel Q?	S/M	1
3	How does bedload vary in shape and size along stream/river Q (from source to mouth)?	M	1
4	A comparative study of meandering and straighter sections of river X.	M	2
5	An investigation into the accuracy and reliability of stream channel measurements.	S	3
6	There is a proportional relationship between channel, meander and flood plain widths in river X.	M/L	2
7	Can channel sinuosity be related to other characteristics of river Y?	M	3
8	After storm events, there is an increase in suspended sediment proportional to the increase in discharge in river channel Z.	S/M	3
9	How do channel characteristics vary above and below key confluences on river X?	S	1
10	There is a positive relationship between sub-catchment size and the exit discharge of several streams draining upland area T.	L	1
11	What is the perception of river/pond/lake X as both an opportunity and a threat in town Y?	S/M	3
12	An evaluation of the river corridor and channel management in a short stretch of river X.	S	3
13	How and why do cliff and beach profiles vary along a stretch of coastline between points X and Y?	M	3
14	How difficult is it to identify and measure waves and wave processes along coastline T?	M	3
15	There is a seasonal relationship between wave energy and the nature of the beach slope and material at Z.	S	2
16	An investigation into the impacts of coastal protection schemes along coastline Z.	M	4
17	What factors make the cliffs vulnerable to collapse and recession along coastal section X?	M	2
18	Is long shore drift a measurable process moving beach material along stretch of coastline Q?	M	4
19	A survey of the sources and distribution of flotsam, jetsam and other waste on the beaches near town X.	S	2
20	What factors influence variation in vegetation patterns across salt marsh Z (or sand dune system Y).	S	1
21	There is a positive relationship between the angle of beach slope and surface beach material size at Q.	S	1
22	People's perception of beach quality at X will vary according to age and activities undertaken.	S	2
23	A study of microclimate variations within small wood T compared to the surrounding open fields.	S	2
24	What is the relationship between evaporation rates and factors such as temperature, windspeed, relative humidity and hours of sunshine in area Z?	S	4
25	Discovery fieldwork within area V seldom generates sufficient and worthwhile physical data.	S/M	4
26	How do barriers such as hedges, fences and trees at site T influence wind speed and direction, and what are the outcomes of this effect?	S	2
27	An analysis of the microclimate variations within the grounds of school/college Q, or around the large building V surrounded by open space.	S	2
28	How and why does a lake or reservoir P modify the microclimate of the area adjacent to it?	S	2
29	How strong is the influence of altitude on the microclimate of hilly area U?	M/L	2
30	An investigation into the reliability and variability of regional weather forecasts through comparisons with local primary data in area X.	L	2
31	An account of the variations in temperature, pressure, cloud cover, wind, precipitation and humidity in garden Z over a period of a month.	S	1
32	How and why do soil characteristics vary down slope S?	S	3
33	There is a direct relationship between infiltration rates and soil texture/structure at sites T, U, V, ...	S	2
34	A comparative study of garden and woodland soils in area X (including environmental influences).	S	2
35	An investigation into the structure and diversity of local woodland Q, including the effects of human activity.	S	2
36	Vegetation at X (part of a heathland/moorland) shows clear signs of adaptation to the environment.	S/M	2
37	Does water depth control the zonation of plants around the margins of lake L?	S	1
38	An analysis of slope variation across a stretch of river valley Y.	S/M	3
39	There is no relationship between scree size, slope angle and slope position at site(s) A, B, C, ...	S	2
40	What factors influence the rates of weathering on several buildings or within graveyards in town X?	S	2
41	What is the impact of rock type Z on the scenery, soils, vegetation and land usage in area Y?	M/L	3
42	A survey of the distribution and orientation of glacial features, such as corries, drumlins or kettle holes in area G.	L	1

Amenity topics

No.	Suggested title	Likely scale	Level of achievability
1	An investigation into the provision and use of recreational amenities in rural area Y.	L	2
2	A survey of the impact of tourism and recreation on Z (a particular site, settlement or area).	S/M	3
3	There is a clear tendency for the more popular visitor attractions in area Q to have more extensive spheres of influence.	M/L	1
4	A study of the differences between visitors and residents in their perceptions of resorts X and Y.	M	2
5	A survey and analysis of the holiday or leisure habits of community X.	S/M	2
6	What are the daily/seasonal patterns of use in open space Y (a large city/town park)?	S	1
7	Local authority landfill sites, such as in area X, tend to have a negative impact zone around them.	M	2
8	An investigation into the scope and viability of recycling facilities in town/village X.	S/M	2
9	A study of the vulnerability of small informal recreational areas in town/village X.	S	3
10	What would be the impact of the expansion or relocation of the football stadium at Z (and/or site Y)?	S/M	2
11	Are countryside parks the way ahead in terms of recreational facilities for urban dwellers in town/city Q?	M/L	4
12	A feasibility study of maintaining service/amenity Z in town/village X.	S	2
13	Is there a relationship between the entrance charges and the quality of visitor amenities in area Q?	M	1

Population topics

No.	Suggested title	Likely scale	Level of achievability
1	A survey of the structure and characteristics of the population of two contrasting urban wards or rural parishes.	M/L	1
2	Population and migration surveys of two contrasting villages X and Y.	M	2
3	A survey to show how and why the population structure of town Y has changed over the last 30 years.	M/L	2
4	A study of a particular demographic group, e.g. ethnic minorities, old age pensioners, upper income groups, to appreciate their distribution in urban area X and to consider the reasons for this.	L	3
5	In rural area Z, there is a tendency for remoter, smaller villages to decline at the expense of larger, more accessible ones.	L	2
6	What factors influence school catchments in area Q?	M	2
7	An evaluation of the demographic transition model as applied to parishes X, Y, Z over the last 100 years.	M/L	3

Rural topics

No.	Suggested title	Likely scale	Level of achievability
1	To what extent do physical factors influence farm practice and land use in area Z or farm Y?	S/M	3
2	A study of the extent and viability of diversification and agricultural innovation in area Z.	M/L	3
3	There is no clear relationship between farm size/land usage and distance from town/city X.	L	1
4	What evidence is there of conflict between agricultural practices and conservation in area Z?	M/L	3
5	Higher order services are confined only to the larger sized settlements in rural area Z.	M/L	1
6	An investigation into perceived, actual and potential land use conflicts at the rural/urban fringe of area Y (or within a designated area of landscape quality, e.g. a National Park).	L	4
7	How strong is the process of gentrification in rural area (or parish) Z?	M/L	3
8	An investigation into how village X has developed over time, including the repercussions of population and service changes.	S/M	2
9	An investigation into the various service catchment areas of the key rural settlement Y.	M	1
10	What evidence exists for the urbanisation of rural settlement Y?	S/M	2
11	Are golf courses generally an environmental, economic and social asset in rural area X?	L	3
12	A comparison of the land-use change over time (period A-B) in two contrasting rural parishes.	M/L	2
13	There is a proportional relationship between settlement population size and catchment in area Z.	M/L	2
14	An investigation into the quality of service provision for the elderly and disabled in area Z.	M/L	2
15	To what extent is village Y self-contained in terms of services, employment and leisure facilities?	S/M	2
16	How important is service X to the life of village Y?	S	1
17	The case for and against living in village Z.	S/M	1
18	What has been the impact of new housing developments in village Z over the last 30 years?	S/M	2
19	Settlements of similar sizes are regularly spaced in rural area Z.	L	1
20	How reasonable are rural planning decisions and restrictions in parish Z?	M/L	3
21	Is there a need for more affordable housing for first-time buyers in village W?	S/M	2

Urban topics

No.	Suggested title	Likely scale	Level of achievability
1	A study of the distribution of vandalism and crime within town Y.	M/L	2
2	An investigation of the factors which have led to the growth of town X, and the degree to which this growth conforms to established urban models.	L	3
3	A survey to determine the limits of the CBD in town X, and to assess the degree to which this conforms to accepted theories such as the Core Frame Model.	M	3
4	A study of the perception and reality of the homeless problem in town X.	M/L	3
5	An investigation to establish the relationship between pedestrian densities, business rates and other factors within the CBD of town X.	M	2
6	A survey of the distribution of particular types of shops within the town centre X.	M	1
7	An investigation into the nature and distribution of recent housing developments in town X.	M	1
8	What factors have influenced house prices in various parts of town X?	M/L	2
9	An evaluation of the various initiatives (e.g. urban renewal schemes) in selected inner-city wards of town/city Z.	M/L	4
10	With increasing distance from the CBD of town/city W, housing density tends to reduce and environmental quality tends to increase.	L	1
11	A comparative study of the demographic, environmental and service differences between urban wards X and Y in town/city Z.	M/L	3
12	What is the impact of a new superstore or urban fringe retail park upon traditional town centre X?	L	4
13	Is there a more rapid turnover of shops in town centre W than X years ago? If so, what factors have influenced this and what issues might arise from it?	M	4
14	Do certain types of shops avoid town centre X, and if so, for what reasons?	M	2
15	A survey of industrial estate W to investigate the reasons why companies have located there.	S/M	2
16	A survey of the changing distribution and impacts of industry over time in town X.	L	2
17	An investigation into the distribution and use of public open space, including allotments, in town Y	M/L	2
18	What is the scope and scale of residential conflict and competition in street Z?	S	4
19	An investigation into the distribution and use of key recreational/sporting facilities in town X.	M/L	2
20	An investigation into the degree of competition between two nearby towns: Y and Z.	L	4
21	The strength of the catchment influence of town X tends to decline with distance away from it.	L	2
22	An explanation of the location and distribution of particular functions such as fast food outlets, charity shops, petrol stations or post offices in town X.	M/L	1
23	The life history and future prospects of derelict or run-down area Z in town Y.	S	1
24	An enquiry into the recent changes at the urban fringe of city/town X, and the related issues.	M/L	2
25	An investigation into the apparent 'health' of town X in terms of employment, population, service/amenity provision, environmental quality, residents' perceptions, etc.	M/L	4
26	What is the nature and extent of urban pollution in selected parts of town X?	M	2
27	An investigation into the role of colour, design and materials in enhancing the urban environment.	L	1
28	Should proposed development Y be allowed to go ahead at site X in town/city Z?	S	2
29	How can you measure the desirability or otherwise of residential districts within town W?	M	2
30	What is the relationship between the distribution of telephone and letter boxes in town X?	M/L	1
31	Functions above street level in town centre W tend to have a higher degree of confidentiality.	M	3
32	Are pedestrianised zones the way ahead for congested town centres such as urban area Z?	S/M	2
33	What are the relative advantages of out-of-town and town centre sites in town X?	M	1
34	What evidence exists for globalisation within town X in terms of goods, services and employment?	L	2
35	To what extent can town X absorb the planned expansion of housing in the near future?	M/L	3
36	A study of people's mental maps of urban area Z, and the reasons for variation between them.	M/L	3
37	There is a significant pattern in the density of chewing-gum marks on the pavements of city/town centre C.	M	1
38	To what extent does town X fit the CBD model in terms of zones of discard and assimilation?	M	3
39	A study of the land-use changes in town centre Y over time period B.	M	1
40	The story of de-industrialisation in area Z: can business/retail parks replace manufacturing industry?	M/L	4
41	An investigation to account for the land-use changes along a transect through town/city X.	S/M	1
42	To what extent does the perception of 'high risk' areas vary by age, gender and type in town/city W?	M/L	3

Q: On these four pages of suggested project titles there are two clues which link to the idea of a universe. Can you solve the secret?

Activity Surveys

Humans are a fairly hyperactive species in general, and as people's mobility and incomes have increased, so their 'activity patterns' have become more diverse and complex. Where once people's everyday activities were limited to their immediate home area, they now tend to range over longer distances: their movements being governed by a mix of factors. This gives you the opportunity to explore the geography of various activities, and in particular to investigate the decisions and perceptions that influence people's movements.

Pedestrian surveys

Such surveys can be conducted in urban areas to find out how and why the density and movement of pedestrians varies in different parts of the urban environment. You would expect an increase in pedestrian numbers as you get closer to the central area.

Where and when to survey
- At a variety of sites within the city/town centre, including
  a) along main routeways where junctions occur, and
  b) along minor routeways including passages and paths (numerical decay may be rapid within a few metres of bustling streets).
- At peak as well as off-peak times.
- Under different weather conditions.
Note: One-off sampling is suspect and may well lead to unreliable conclusions.

How to survey
1. By counting the number of people (a 'foot-fall' count) who pass by each site during a 15-20 minute period. The counts must take place at the same time for all the sites, so many people will be needed

for this exercise. It is best to work in pairs, covering both sides of a routeway if applicable, and counting people moving in either direction. Pedestrianised zones pose a problem since the volumes may be very high and difficult to record accurately at certain times of the day. Also, people may be 'milling' rather than moving directionally. You will need to decide on a strategy for dealing with this before you start.

2. By walking at a steady pace (an 'on the hoof' count) along a 50-100m stretch of pavement and recording all pedestrians that you pass, including stationary ones, and all those who pass you. A click-counter is useful for this exercise. While doing this, you may be able to undertake a route quality survey (see page 86) and to link it to areas of pavement which are under- or over-used.

Analysing the results
- For 'foot-fall' surveys, pool the information

gathered and map it using **isolines**. The resulting pattern (Figure 1) should reflect the fact that accessibility, desirability and concentration of shops in the core area of the CBD attracts the highest pedestrian densities. Low pedestrian densities may be associated with non-retail zones, or with more run-down areas ('zones of discard') which may be characterised by lower environmental quality, a higher turnover of shop premises, a prevalence of empty premises and short-lease shops, and higher rates of crime (actual or perceived).

- For 'on the hoof' surveys, plot the recorded data in the form of flow lines of proportional widths.

Pedestrian zone — Main road
Sampling point — Minor road

Figure 1: An isoline map of a 15min town centre pedestrian survey.

Space-time surveys

These are surveys of daily movements, usually made over a period of one week. The idea is to compare activity patterns between different groups or individuals, and to see what factors affect their behaviour (e.g. level of income and mobility; age; cultural factors such as ethnicity; size of family; occupation).

How to survey
1. For your survey, it is important to choose **respondents** whose characteristics enable you to focus on the **variables** you are most interested in, and to cancel out others which might affect daily movements. So, for example, if you are interested in the impact of income level

on activity patterns, the age as well as the ethnicity and area of residence of your respondents should be similar.

2. Ask the chosen respondents to log in a diary their weekly movements from home (the central point) to various destinations (Figures 2a and 2b). The log should include information on the distance to each destination, and the time taken to get there.

3. The logged information must be supplemented by information from interviews with the

respondents. The interviews should be used to find out about respondents' motives and preferences for the movements they make (see also page 64).

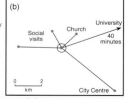
UP TO ONE WEEK

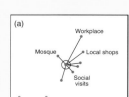

Both respondents have similar income levels and live in the same inner-city ward. (Both travel on foot, by car and use public transport.) Observe the different patterns which reflect their differing lifestyles.

Figure 2: (a) Islamic shop assistant (24 years), and (b) Catholic student (21 years).

Recreational surveys

Where to survey
- Town and country parks and playgrounds
- Rivers and canals, including adjacent pathways
- Rural **honeypot sites** or beauty spots
- Leisure centres and swimming pools
- Beaches, lakes and reservoirs

Surveying and plotting results
- For each location, record the number of users over a one-hour period, classifying them by age, gender and user-type (e.g. elderly male dog-walker). Try to conduct surveys at different times and under different weather conditions to enable comparisons to be made.

The recreational activities observed can be categorised in various ways:
>   Active/Passive
>   Indoor/Outdoor
>   Formal/Informal
>   Zero/Low/Medium/High Impact

For example, walking a dog along a canal tow-path can be described as an active, outdoor, informal medium impact activity (as the dog can bark and annoy other users).

- Consider making an impact **matrix** (Figure 3) which subjectively assesses how the recorded activities interact both with each other and with the local community and environment.
- On a large-scale base map of the survey area, you could plot various movements made by the site users. For example, at honeypot sites if you can gain a vantage point above the main car park you could note the furthest point reached by each site user and plot it on your map with a dot. The dots could be colour coded according to gender or activity (some National Park surveys have revealed that up to 90% of users do not go beyond eyesight of their vehicles).

- The basic surveys need to be supported by primary data which can be gathered using, e.g.

questionnaires for visitors; interviews with visitors, site managers/ wardens. The primary data could include: duration of stay; distance travelled to the site (a good clue is a garage sticker on a car window, telling you where the car was bought (**provenance**)); frequency of visits; motives for visiting; the pros and cons of that particular **amenity** site – including related issues such as facilities, access, overcrowding, litter, noise, erosion, vandalism, etc.

- From the information gathered, **sphere of influence** maps at the 50%, 75% and 95% levels could be constructed (Figure 4). You could also produce an evaluation and management plan for the site.

Overall, a very tidy project.

Activity

✓ = peaceful co-existence
? = uncertain impact
✗ = negative mix

Activity	Pedestrians and joggers	Sun-bathers	Dog-walkers	Rollerbladers and cyclists	Children's playground	Anglers	Group of youths	Environment	Community
Pedestrians and joggers	-	✓	?	✗	✓	✓	✓	✓	✓
Sun-bathers	✓	-	?	✓	✓	✓	?	✓	✓
Dog-walkers	?	?	-	✗	✓	?	✓	?	✓
Rollerbladers and cyclists	✗	✓	✗	-	✓	✓	✓	✓	✓
Children's playground	✓	✓	✓	✓	-	✓	✗	✓	?
Anglers	✓	✓	?	✓	✓	-	✓	?	✓
Group of youths	✓	?	✓	✓	✗	✓	-	?	?

Figure 3: Riverside Park impact matrix.

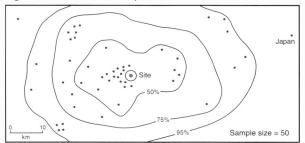

Figure 4: Sphere of influence map.

Amenity surveys

These can overlap with recreational surveys.

Surveying and processing results
- Select a definable area for which **Census** statistics can be obtained, e.g. a rural parish, a town or a district. Through direct observation and local knowledge, and using secondary sources such as large-scale maps, *Yellow Pages* and local advertisements, map the location and provision of **amenities** (e.g. sports pitches, playgrounds, sports halls, parks and gardens, telephone/pillar boxes, schools, cinemas, clubs and pubs).
- Conduct user surveys to estimate the level and frequency of usage, and relate these figures to the total population within that Census area. This gives the assumed threshold figure: i.e. if there are eight pubs in a parish of 2000 people, the notional average level of custom is 250 people per pub. In reality, customers can go to more than one pub, and not all people are drinkers or of drinking age, so the threshold figure is very rough.

Your project should concentrate on the factors that make particular amenities viable

and attractive (or otherwise). For example, some pubs exceed their threshold figure because of a reputation for real ale, good food and conviviality, for which

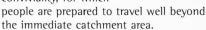

people are prepared to travel well beyond the immediate catchment area.

Comparing high and low seasons at a tourist resort

- For a chosen resort, obtain a list of accommodation (on- and off-season), and information about its main attractions and amenities.
- Map the various retail and commercial functions of the resort, and the main amenities. Highlight those which are closed in the off-season.
- Conduct a questionnaire survey of both tourists and local residents to evaluate the quality of the tourist amenities and related seasonal issues.

'UK national parks – impact of tourism', *Geography Review*, vol. 11, no. 5, May 1998.

page **15**

Air Quality Assessment

Our atmosphere, a mixture of gases and dust surrounding the Earth, is a vital physical system. It maintains a supply of oxygen to support life, it controls the Earth's heat budget and it blocks out most of the harmful solar energy. It also has the remarkable ability to absorb and clean up waste materials or pollutants such as volcanic ash and radioactive contamination.

Ever since the Industrial Revolution of the eighteenth century, the global effects of vehicular, domestic, industrial and agricultural processes have been steadily growing. The levels of concentration reached by some of these pollutants are such that the atmosphere can no longer maintain a healthy balance. There are cheap and simple ways of monitoring some of these pollutants locally – you may be surprised by what you find.

Limitations

- Sensitive monitoring equipment will often not be available for your use – generally such equipment is used only by universities, local authorities and specialist agencies/companies.

- In terms of secondary data, little may be available to you at the local scale, though regionally and nationally it is plentiful (see ICT links).

More about air pollution

The major pollutants in the atmosphere are a mixture of nitrogen oxides (known as NO_x gases) and carbon dioxide (CO_2) both derived from combustion in vehicle engines (as are hydrocarbons and trace heavy metals). Sulphur dioxide (SO_2) is another major pollutant, which comes mainly from coal-fired power stations. Acid deposition is a particular type of SO_2 **pollution**, which comes in two forms: wet deposition (e.g. rain, snow) and dry deposition, which is the direct absorption of gases by plants. Particulate air pollution is evident in the dirt on windows and the atmospheric haze above large urban areas or industrial plants – particularly at sunset.

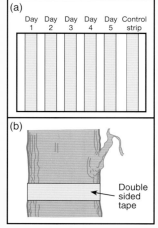

Equipment

UP TO ONE WEEK

- Plastic funnel, filter paper, collecting bottle or rain gauge
- Masking tape/double-sided adhesive tape
- Microscope

Particulates

These are small particles of air-borne soot, dead skin, ash, pollen and so on. The largest concentrations are in industrialised urban environments, particularly along congested routeways. Ideally, samples of particulates should be taken as close as possible to the point sources of pollution, preferably in a line down-wind. However, since your sampling equipment may 'walk' or get crushed by people and animals, a safer alternative is to use several locations that are more secure, such as the top of school/college buildings, gardens and woodlands.

1. Fold a piece of filter paper, insert it into a plastic funnel and place this into a milk bottle or rain gauge (Figure 1). Leave it out at until there has been a rain shower. Particulates will be deposited on the paper as rain water passes through. Remove and label the filter paper and then oven-dry at about 100°C (low gas mark) overnight. Carefully remove the particulates with a soft brush and weigh them using a sensitive pan balance, accurate to 0.01

gram. It may be possible to work out the mass of particulates for a given volume of precipitation if you use a rain gauge. You can also examine the particles under a microscope to determine size and nature of material.

2. Mount an A5 piece of white card on to a similar sized rectangle of hardboard and attach a stake to the board so that it can be secured to the ground. Stick on six 2cm strips of masking tape (Figure 2a), one for each day of the school week, plus one as a **control**. Remove one strip each day. At the end of the week remove the control strip and compare the density of particulate coverage underneath this and the other five strips, both visually and under a microscope (where you may be able to quantify the degree of coverage). The first strip removed should have the most particulate coverage at the end of the survey period.

3. Instead of 2. above, you

could wrap double-sided adhesive tape (carpet tape) around standing objects at 2-3m above ground level, beyond passing reach (e.g. telegraph poles, lamp posts and trees) (Figure 2b). Remove the tape at weekly intervals and examine the sticky surface, as for 2. above.

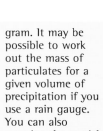

Cone shaped filter paper in plastic funnel

Milk bottle or rain guage

Bury in the ground to stabilise

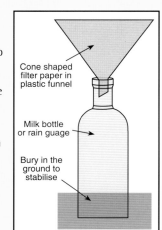

(a)

| Day 1 | Day 2 | Day 3 | Day 4 | Day 5 | Control strip |

(b)

Double sided tape

Figure 1 (left): Particulate collection in rain gauge/bottle.
Figure 2 (right): Particulate comparison using (a) masking tape and cardboard, and (b) double-sided sticky tape.

Lenon, B. and Cleves, P. (1994) *Fieldwork Techniques in Geography*. Collins Educational, pages 68-73.

Acid rain

1. **Wet monitoring:** The simplest way to monitor **acid rain** is to collect rainwater in a rain gauge, or use a plastic bottle cut in half, with the lower half sunk 15cm into the ground. Always wash the container or rain gauge with de-ionised water and cover the opening with a piece of gauze to prevent contamination by leaves, etc. Test the **pH** of the water with a pH meter or pH strips. You want to be accurate to a least 0.5 pH as the changes in the levels of pH may be very slight. Monitor at different times and dates.

Strongly acidic, pH 4.0 rain which is acidified	Weak acid, pH 5.6, 'natural' rainwater	Chemically neutral, pH 7.0, e.g. milk

2. **Dry monitoring:** Lichens are very simple plants which grow on bare rock, trees and even concrete surfaces (some look like paint splodges, others are more like

Equipment
- Plastic funnel, collecting bottle or rain gauge
- pH meter or strips, gauze
- Lichen key (Appendix), gauze

VARIABLE

moss). They are good **indicator species** of air pollution, especially SO_2 as this affects both the growth rates and the species type. Refer to the Appendix (page 107 for SO_2 tolerance levels of certain lichens, and a simple identification key.

Noise pollution

Unless you have access to a decibel meter (dB), noise pollution measurements can only be subjective. You can use a scale such as that in Figure 3, or devise your own. Possible survey sites are:

- noisy environments such as major road junctions, railways stations, airports, construction sites
- quieter areas such as residential streets, graveyards, moorland/mountain areas, woodlands.

In the case of noisy places, try to measure how the noise levels decay with distance from the source. (Note: This will vary according to time of day and the direction and strength of the wind.) Comment on measures that have been taken to reduce noise pollution (e.g. concrete barriers/ wooden fences and cuttings to baffle motorway noise). If possible, make

Equipment
- Decibel meter
- Recording sheets
- Ear protectors

UP TO TWO HOURS

measurements to test their effectiveness.
An increase of 20dB is approximate to a noise which is 100 times greater! For prolonged exposure to 85dB or above, ear protectors should be worn.

Score	Decibels (dB)	Description
7	140	Deafeningly loud, e.g. jumbo jet taking off
6	120	Very loud, e.g. a live pop band
5	100	Loud, e.g. a heavy lorry passing by
4	80	Noisy, e.g. main traffic routes at busy times
3	60	Quiet, e.g. a normal conversation
2	40	Very quiet, e.g. a library
1	20	Barely audible, e.g. a ticking watch

Figure 3: Example scales for noise level.

Other ideas

You could also consider investigating **ozone**, smell or pollen levels. The equipment you need depends on the investigation. It will take you up to two weeks of repeat sampling (sniffing in the case of smell pollution) and recording to gather sufficient data.

Ozone

The ozone in the upper atmosphere protects the Earth from the sun's ultraviolet rays, but at ground level it can be harmful to human health and plant tissue if it occurs in high concentrations. It is largely produced by the chemical reaction of NO_2 with atmospheric oxygen in the presence of bright sunshine (the effects are therefore more pronounced in summer). Certain plant species, such as *Nicotiana tabacum* (cultivar Bel-W3), are ozone-sensitive and can be used as indicators. However, a simpler way of measuring ozone concentrations is to use detector cards such as those produced by Dryden Aqua of Edinburgh (website: http://www.1x1x1.co.uk). Five cards cost about £10.

Smell pollution

Our perceptions of what are good and bad smells, and strong or minor smells vary a great deal depending on such things as cultural norms and nasal sensitivity. Obvious examples of things that we all tend to notice as having an unpleasant or strong smell are body odour, traffic fumes, farmyard slurries and the outputs of some industrial processes. Whatever scale you devise to measure smells will be subjective and crude, but it can still be useful. For example, you could have a scale of 0-5 where:

0 = no smell detectable
1 = at this level you could do without it, but it is barely noticeable
5 = highly offensive, inducing a strong reaction

Pollen

When breathed in, pollen can cause unpleasant hay-fever type symptoms in some people. This is why pollen counts are published by the media at peak times. Flowering crops (e.g. oil-seed rape) produce large quantities of pollen so counts vary according to current agricultural practices and policies. Primary data collection is not usually practical so use figures published in newspapers and on television, you can also obtain information on pollen counts from the BBC website: http://www.bbc.co.uk/ weather/features/pollen.shtml.

ICT links

The following website has lots of air quality information and statistics for the UK: http://www.aeat.co.uk/netcen/airqual

For current air quality information, try Ceefax pages 410-17 or Teletext page 106.

Field Studies Council fold out key on Lichens. FSC 1998, (see page 111 for address).

Beach and Coastal Surveys

Our group of Atlantic islands has largely been shaped by the sea – it's a dynamic and changing environment that includes over 10 000 miles (16 000km) of coastal landforms. The pace and nature of change is influenced by a wide range of forces, both human and physical. These forces may have dramatic consequences for both lives and landscapes, necessitating coastal management and strategic planning, but also offering plenty of scope for fieldwork. Coasts are a core area of study in the new coursework specifications, so consider a day or two by the sea, and read on ...

Limitations

- In many coastal surveys, the tidal conditions (low, high, spring, neap) may be an important consideration both for reasons of access to the field survey site and for safety.
- If you live in Coventry, for example, it is a long trip to the nearest coastline (over 100km).
- Some coastal surveys only work well 'in season', e.g. tourist surveys in August and ecosystem surveys in May/June.

Coastal fieldwork – the range of options

1. Identifying and measuring waves, winds and currents.

2. Visitor surveys in tourist resorts. Beach quality surveys.

3. Measuring beach slopes, particle sizes, pebble shapes and sorting.

4. Studies of small-scale **ecosystems**, including succession and management, e.g. salt marshes and sand dunes.

5. Sketching/photographing, explaining and evaluating coastal protection schemes (including flooding) with **cost-benefit analysis** and attitude surveys.

6. Surveying heights and slopes of cliffs. Sketching cliff profiles including geology, structure, mass movement, erosional processes and rates of recession.

7. Assessment of inshore water quality.

Safety first

Coastal areas are potentially very dangerous, so special care and forward planning are needed to ensure your safety. Take special note of the following, as well as the usual safety precautions (see page 9):

- Be aware of the state of the tides, particularly along cliff sections, headlands and wide beaches. Consult Tide Timetables and watch out for spring or storm high tides and the rate of the incoming tide. Every year people get cut off in this way, sometimes attempting to climb out up dangerous cliffs.

- Watch out for and avoid slippery rocks on the foreshore at low tide.

- Beware of animal and human waste, both on beaches and in the sea.

- Avoid working near the foot of cliffs, especially crumbling ones, and wear a hard hat if appropriate.

- Keep well back from cliff tops, particularly in wet and windy conditions.

- Measuring waves can be dangerous – make sure you do it from a safe and secure position and watch out for freak waves which might sweep you away.

'Coastal management in north-east Norfolk', *Geography Review*, vol. 9, no. 5, May 1996.

Wave surveys

Waves are largely created by winds. The energy of waves is related to their size and frequency – the higher and more frequent the waves, the more energetic or destructive their effect (Figure 1).

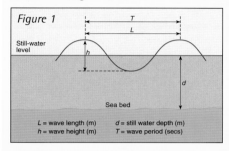

Figure 1

Still-water level

L = wave length (m)   d = still water depth (m)
h = wave height (m)   T = wave period (secs)

Wave frequency

From a good vantage point, count the number of breaking waves in a five minute period. Repeat several times and calculate the mean. Constructive or spilling waves are generally below 13 per minute (pm), while destructive waves are above 13 pm.

Wave period

This is the time interval between each passing wave crest or breaking wave. Simply divide the frequency into 60 seconds, e.g. frequency of 20 pm = wave period of 3 seconds.

Wave height

From a safe position, lower a metre ruler or a ranging pole into the water (Figure 2). Read off the approximate wave crest and trough positions and subtract one from the other to give the wave height in metres. Repeat several times and calculate the mean. (You may be able to observe waves moving past a fixed object like a jetty chain, rope or ladder, and to estimate their height). Note that wave heights may vary according to the state of the tide (greatest at high tide).

Wave length

This can be calculated if the approximate water depth is known:

Deeper water (depth is more than $1/2$ wavelength): wave length in metres = (wave period)^2 x 1.56.

Shallower water (depth is less than $1/2$ wavelength): wave length = wave period x 3.13 x square root of water depth. (Measure water depth mid-way between the crests and the troughs – Figure 1.)

Longshore drift

This current is experienced in most open bays where wave fronts have been 'bent' or refracted by headlands and protruding obstructions. These fronts often arrive at a low or oblique angle to the beach, allowing a lateral shift of beach material. There is usually a dominant drift direction which can be observed and measured in the following ways:

a) using differential beach heights: i.e. the difference in the height of beach material on either side of groynes or jetties which trap beach material on the higher or updrift side (Figure 2). These differential

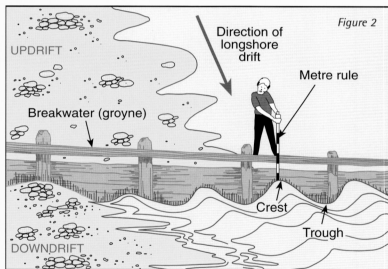

Figure 2

Direction of longshore drift

UPDRIFT

Breakwater (groyne)

Metre rule

Crest

Trough

DOWNDRIFT

heights will vary along groynes, being at their lowest level towards the seaward end of them.

b) by plotting pebble movement using brightly painted marker pebbles or corks under high tide conditions (the markers can be of different sizes and weights. Corks are best since they are more responsive to swash and backwash movements). Mark the start position with a ranging pole, selecting a clear stretch of beach without obstructions. Place the markers within the active or break zone and see what happens over the next 15-30 minutes. Many will be lost by being drawn into deeper water, some may even move in the other direction, and others will become lodged or trapped on the beach. However, you may be able to track enough markers to estimate both the direction and rate of longshore drift. Consider what other factors come into play here, i.e. steepness of beach, nature of beach material, tidal or wind conditions, size and weight of markers, obstructions

c) by noting wind speed and direction (see page 52-53)

Tourist/amenity surveys

Typically, surveys are used to enable comparisons to be made between quite different coastal locations, or between high and low season in one particular place. There are two main approaches:

1. A study of the impact of tourism on a coastal area in terms of population numbers, retail/commercial activities, employment, amenities, car parking and congestion, litter, noise, etc. (see 'Activity Surveys' pages 14-15).
2. Quality assessment surveys of amenity

provision, particularly beaches (see 'Judgement Surveys' pages 42-45).

Some points to note when planning a survey:

- If using questionnaires, make sure your sample size is large enough, and that as well as asking basic questions such as 'How did you travel here?' and 'How often have you visited this resort?' you also try to find out about tourists' perceptions and expectations, what they see as the pros and cons of the resort area, and how they rate the amenity provision. The responses will vary between age groups, since senior citizens

have a very different agenda from teenagers.

- Don't assume you can do this 'on the side' while on a beach holiday with family or friends: you will lack motivation and you will need to research secondary information well ahead of time.

Lenon, B. and Cleves, P. (1994) *Fieldwork Techniques in Geography.* Collins Educational, pages 46-49.

Beach surveys

Beach profiles

Beaches seldom maintain uniform and stable slopes, they are continually being re-worked and re-shaped by wave action. Beach profiles are best done at low tide when the greatest range of material is exposed (Figure 3).

Using at least two ranging poles, a clinometer (Figure 4) and measuring tape, record the gradient and distance between each distinct **'break in slope'** working upbeach from the water's edge (see page 37). Make sure that you keep to the line of the **transect** – place clear markers at the start and finish points. If done accurately you will be able to construct multiple beach cross-sections on graph paper. (Pantometers (Figure 5) can by used by one person and allow a more detailed study since every 1 or 2 metres can be surveyed systematically.)

Possible parallel studies:

1. The relationship between beach slope and beach material size. Generally, the larger the material the more stable it is and the higher angles of repose it will give – resulting in steeper beach slopes (an example of a positive relationship) (see Figure 6).

2. The relationships between wave type, wave energy and beach slope.

Particle sizes

- Systematically sample the beach material every 2-4m up the same transect line used for profiling, or stratify the sampling technique at 'break in slope' points and at the mid-points of each slope segment. At each survey site select 10 surface pebbles which are touching your foot, or use a gridded quadrat (50cm x 50cm) and select the particles nearest to the middle of 10 out of the 25 squares. (This type of sampling breaks down where there is a chaos of both very small and large particles at the same site.) It helps to number your ten samples with a felt pen before removing them for measuring.

- Use a stoneboard (Figure 7) for measuring the three axes of each pebble, or use a clear plastic ruler or even a pebbleometer. Average out the axes to give mean particle size (mps), or just use the long 'a' axis. Assess the degree of roundness of each pebble by using Power's scale of classes 1-6. Then use the semi-circular arcs (Cailleux's scale) to record radius of curvature of the sharpest point of each particle (you can estimate to one mm).

- Use a recording sheet similar to Figure 8 to record details of the 10 pebbles at each survey site. From these calculations, a cross-section of the beach can be drawn with line graphs representing the variation in mps and index of roundness 'in line' below it. The mean values resulting from the various transects (downshore, longshore and repeat visits under different seasonal conditions) will give an insight into the degree of sorting of beach material by wave action in both downshore and longshore directions. Generally, coarser material will be found towards the back of the beaches and on ridges and berms, as well as concentrating towards the downdrift end of beaches. Can you account for this?

Of course, the presence of obstructions such as groynes will interfere with beach material movements and possibly obscure the natural patterns that should exist.

Notes

- Make sure you take along a calculator for the mean values and the index of roundness, and double-check any suspect calculations. You can simplify the operation by not including mps or by taking a smaller sample.

- Work to the nearest millimetre only (correct to one significant decimal place in terms of centimetres), e.g. 5.65cm=5.7cm.

- In reality the shape scale (Powers) will be dominated by classes 5/6, particularly on storm beaches with high wave energies.

- Return all of your samples to exactly the same spot from where they were removed.

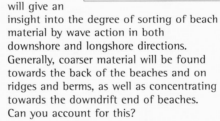

The Index of Roundness (R) $= \frac{2r}{a} \times 1,000$

where r = radius of curvature in mm
where a = length of long axis in mm

Note that values of R above 500 indicate a high degree of roundness, due to the active role of attrition.

A value of a 1000 =

Equipment
- Stopwatch, calculator
- Recording sheets, graph paper
- Ranging poles, 30m tape
- Clinometer, Pantometer
- Quadrat, stoneboard
- Clear plastic ruler or pebbleometer

UP TO **HALF A DAY**

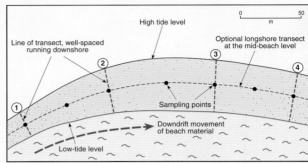

Figure 3: Mapping transects across a beach.

Improvised clinometer
Saw a notch into a 1cm wide, 12cm long thin bar of wood. Ease a 10cm plastic protractor into this notch, so that it jams when inverted. As in Figure 5, attach a sighting eye-hole, a sighting pin and a short length of weighted plumb line secured to the wooden bar exactly in the middle. The plumb line must hang free of the protractor.

Figure 4: An improvised clinometer.

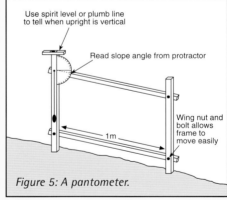

Figure 5: A pantometer.

Beach material	Particle size range (long axis in mm)	Approximate beach slope (in degrees) = angle of repose	Typical gradients
Boulders	>500	?	?
Cobbles	100-500	20-25	1:4
Pebbles	20-100	15-20	1:6
Shingle	2-20	10-15	1:8
Coarse sand	1-2	Up to 10	1:10
Fine sand	0.1-1.0	2/3	1:40
Silt/mud	<0.1	<2	<1:50

Figure 6: Relationship of beach material to beach slope.

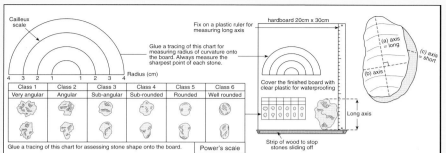

Figure 7: A stoneboard.

Figure 8: Recording sheet.

Location... Name(s)..
Transect no .... Length .... Date/time .... Low tide ....

Site No.	Distance from sea (m)	Slope angle		Samples (cms)											Mean (a) axis	Mean m.p.s	Range m.p.s	Mean Index of roundness
				1	2	3	4	5	6	7	8	9	10					
1	4	1.5°	(a)														smallest	
			(b)															
			(c)															
			m.p.s															
			1-6															
			r															
			R														largest	

Ecosystem surveys

A wide variety of ecosystems and habitats can be found in coastal areas, many of which may be small-scale and fragile. Sand dunes, rock pools and saltwater marshes are examples.

Sand dunes (psammosere)
(see 'Vegetation Surveys' page 94-95)
1. Produce a large-scale sketch map of the dune area, with transect lines and sampling points marked on, as well as access roads, amenities and car park(s). Include a scale.

2. Survey the site, and mark on the **desire lines** of movement from the car park(s) to the beach through the dune system (also assess the capacity of the car park). These pathways may carry evidence of management. Mark the position of interpretation boards, notices and signposts. Identify and describe any other evidence of dune management, e.g. fenced-off zones (particularly extensive areas of bare sand known as blow-out hollows), replanting of marram grass, boardwalks, vehicle barriers, consolidation at the base of unstable dunes, supervision by conservation officers.

3. Conduct a user survey at summer weekends and weekdays noting the number and age of the visitors, and the types of activity they engage in. Make particular note of the ways in which

visitors affect the natural habitat (e.g. litter, trampling of dune grass).

4. Try to find (e.g. in the local library) historical photographs of the dune system to see if any obvious changes have occurred over time (e.g. car park, eroded footpaths, blow-out hollows).

5. Prepare a report on the overall 'health' of the dune system and suggest what type of management (if any) is needed to preserve the ecosystem.

Salt marshes (halosere)
Salt marshes are too small-scale to constitute a coursework project in themselves – they need to be linked to other local ecosystems and local issues such as the building of a tidal barrage or marina; oil spills; reclamation of land for agriculture. They are mostly found in low-lying and sheltered estuary locations where they provide a most cost-effective form of sea defence. Mud flats are colonised by salt-tolerant algae and grasses (e.g. Spartina) which gradually bring about a

Equipment

UP TO ONE DAY

- Recording sheets

conversion from mud flat to salt marsh through the process of **succession**. Such marshes are characterised by a maze of creeks. (Safety note: These can be hazardous sites to work in due to quicksand conditions and the speed of the incoming tide.)

- Take transects at low tide and use a quadrat to sample the vegetation zones at systematic intervals. Identify the plants and take two soil samples – one from the slob zone and one from the sward zone (Figure 9). Analyse these using the methods described in 'Soil Surveys' page 81, (don't expect a wide diversity of vegetation) and compare your results with Figure 9 (an example of a succession model).

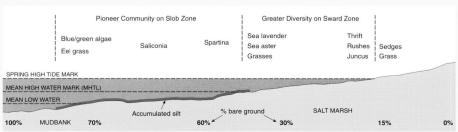

Figure 9: Sketch of plant zones on mud flats/salt marshes.

'Saltmarshes and succession', *Geography Review*, vol. 12, no. 1, September 1998.

page 21

Coastal protection surveys

The more coastal areas are intensively developed (and more capital invested), the greater the need to protect and defend them from destructive wave energy and coastal flooding. This provides opportunities to investigate the appropriateness and effectiveness of such schemes. Figures 10 and 11 show some of the many ways in which this can be done.

Select a coastal strip which contains a range of protection schemes, and where the intensity of land usage varies from very high (resort towns and ports/harbours) to medium (smaller settlements and road/rail routeways) to low (caravan parks and golf courses) to very low (undeveloped land). In this way you can compare protected and unprotected areas.

1. Produce a land use map of the study area which is colour-coded by **function** (see Land Utilisation Key on page 105) and zoned according to the intensity of land usage. Mark on to this map any direct evidence of coastal defensive schemes, and any areas of conservation status (Heritage Coastline, dedicated footpaths, **SSSIs**, historic buildings, etc).

2. Research archive material such as historical maps, photographs, postcards, past copies of local newspapers. These may give an insight into the development of the area over time, and in particular changes in the beach and coastal **morphology** (at best it might reveal the extent of land and building loss). The local or county planning authority may hold details of past or proposed feasibility studies undertaken by consultant engineers, as well as hard facts on the existing coastal schemes and the approximate local land values.

3. Conduct your own survey of the coastal protection schemes in terms of cost, condition, effectiveness, visual quality, etc., and support this with a questionnaire survey/values analysis of the local residents' perception of:
   - the coastal threat
   - the response by the authorities
   - the impact of the coastal defences

   Try to arrange an interview with a local planner.

4. You could evaluate these schemes using a **cost-benefit analysis**, perhaps in association with EIAs (see pages 32-33). The aim is to view the total cost of a scheme over its lifespan in relation to the total costs that would have been incurred if the scheme had not been implemented (i.e. benefits) (Figure 12). For example, a benefit-cost ratio of 1.5 suggests that a protection scheme is viable – the likely benefits following its installation will be half as much again as the costs of the scheme itself. In reality many of the impacts are almost impossible to

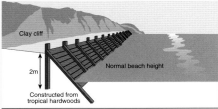

Figure 11: (a) revetments, and (b) sea wall/groynes.

Equipment

- Large-scale maps of area
- Camera/sketch pad
- Questionnaires if appropriate
- Calculator

UP TO TWO DAYS

quantify in cash terms so you will have to use notional figures.

Note: Authorities are reluctant to undertake protection schemes unless they can be justified on economic grounds. With severe budgetary constraints, they generally opt for either:

- low-cost, short-term 'patch solutions' which may transfer the problem elsewhere to areas controlled by other authorities; or

- a strategy of managed retreat which involves the abandonment of coastal stretches of low intensity usage. This is an extremely cheap and environmentally friendly solution since, over time, beaches and salt marshes will develop. These act as natural defences against further erosion and flooding.

Costs	Benefits
Construction of scheme	Protection of infrastructure
Ongoing maintenance	Protection of farmland/buildings
Purchase of land	Protection of tourist amenities, e.g. beaches
Compensation	Reduction of flood risk
Loss of visual quality	'Peace of mind' for residents
Knock-on effects	Reduced cost of emergency services

Figure 12 (above): A cost-benefit analysis.

Figure 10 (below): Different methods of coastal protection.

Coastal scheme	Typical location and function	Approximate costings (mid-1990s)	Typical lifespan (years)	Possible outcomes
Concrete sea-walls	Popular sea-side resorts. Double up as promenades.	£5000 per metre	50-75	Deflect waves downwards and increase beach erosion, eventually undermining the sea wall.
Revetments	Lower cost defences along less developed coastlines.	£2000 per metre	Less than 50 years	Effective at breaking and absorbing wave energy, but do not give complete protection.
Groynes	On tourist beaches, spaced every 100-200m.	£10,000 each	25-40	Trap and maintain sand on tourist beaches, but may lead to sediment starvation downdrift.
Gabions	Boulder-filled wire cages often behind sea walls or revetments.	£500 per metre	10-30	Rapidly break up if exposed to high wave energies. Over time they can be stabilised by vegetation.
Earth embankments	Flood defences along low-lying, low intensity coastlines.	£1000 per metre	Variable	Protect farmland, but prevent the sea from encroaching inland, finding its line of equilibrium.
Rip-rap	Huge piled boulders, patching up earlier failed schemes.	£1000 each rock	Short-term	Huge mass prevents movement in storm waves, gaps absorb wave energy.
Beach feeding	Gravel/sand dumped by local authorities on tourist beaches.	Cheap	Short-term	Easily removed by offshore currents and longshore drift.

Cliff surveys

These can be dangerous! You may decide to undertake a risk assessment of the site first (see pages 68-69).

Cliff geology and structure

(Refer to a local geological guide or map if possible.) Try to take photos of the cliff site, and make a rough sketch of it (Figure 13). Annotate the sketch with as many of the following elements as possible, and include an approximate scale:

1. Obvious features – caves, stacks, wave-cut notch and platform, gullying, beach width and slope, high tide level, basal boulders etc.

2. Basic geology – try to identify the various rock types (as in Figure 13).

3. Basic structure – evidence of **bedding planes** (including thickness and angle of dip), jointing, folding and faulting of the rock layers (known as strata) (Figure 14).

4. Evidence of erosion – differential erosion where weaker rock layers such as coal or shale may form a notch in the cliff profile, or undercut (wave cut) notches at the cliff foot, or gullying of the cliff face.

5. Mass movement – evidence of slumping, mudslides or rock fall especially in clays/sands and in strongly bedded or jointed rock.

6. Basal activity – how active is cliff-foot erosion by the sea, and how does the rate of removal of dislodged material compare with the rate of accumulation at the cliff-foot?

7. Built structures at the cliff-foot, on the face, or at the cliff top (evidence of drainage, stabilisation and protection schemes).

8. The degree of vegetation cover and type – note any animal activity.

Recession rates

In some areas you can observe signs of recession in the landscape (e.g. collapsed features such as wartime gun emplacements) but historical maps and/or written records are the best sources. Spits are some of the most active areas of coastline (Figure 15). As a general rule, hard igneous rocks such as granite will recede at average rates of less than 1mm per year. Well-jointed or soluble hard rocks such as limestone and chalk may average several centimetres per year, while unconsolidated clays and sands may recede on average by more than a metre per year, as in parts of the Holderness and Norfolk coastlines. This recession is not a gradual activity – it occurs in occasional 'quantum leaps' usually due to saturated cliffs and winter storms. The less the cliff-foot protection (particularly natural beaches), the greater the probability of undercutting and mass movement, resulting in

Equipment
- Geological guides
- Camera

UP TO TWO HOURS

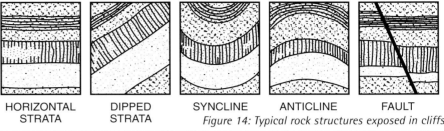

HORIZONTAL STRATA DIPPED STRATA SYNCLINE ANTICLINE FAULT

Figure 14: Typical rock structures exposed in cliffs

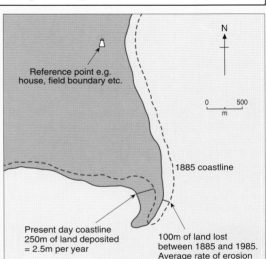

N

Reference point e.g. house, field boundary etc.

0   500
m

1885 coastline

Present day coastline 250m of land deposited = 2.5m per year

100m of land lost between 1885 and 1985. Average rate of erosion = 1m per year

Figure 15: Measuring coastal change, Spurn Head, Holderness.

greater rates of recession.

The cliff profile reflects not only the rock type(s) it is made of, but also the other forces acting upon it: sub-aerial **weathering**, mass-movement, basal erosion by the sea, and human activity. Cliffs will tend to have a lower profile where they are made of softer rock and where the rates of accumulation at the base are greater than the rates of removal by the sea. The size and nature of the beach, the wave cut platform (if any), the high-tide level and the typical wave energies involved are all crucial factors in this equation.

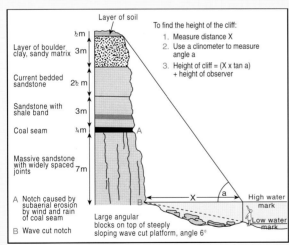

Layer of soil

½m

Layer of boulder clay, sandy matrix 3m

Current bedded sandstone 2½ m

Sandstone with shale band 3m

Coal seam ¼m

Massive sandstone with widely spaced joints 7m

A Notch caused by subaerial erosion by wind and rain of coal seam

B Wave cut notch

To find the height of the cliff:
1. Measure distance X
2. Use a clinometer to measure angle a
3. Height of cliff = (X x tan a) + height of observer

A

X   a   High water mark

B   Low water mark

Large angular blocks on top of steeply sloping wave cut platform, angle 6°

Figure 13: A cliff profile.

Inshore water surveys

You may wish to include inshore water surveys as part of your enquiry. A focus for such surveys could be **pollution**, noting (and photographing) such things as chemical froth, waste flotsam and jetsam, oil pollution and sewage contamination. You could also record daily sea temperatures and compare them to air temperatures.

The EU officially classifies dirty beaches as exceeding 2000 faecal colleiform bacteria per 100ml of bathing water. This and other information is displayed on all tourist beaches – those that have passed the basic EU standards carry the Blue Flag. There are currently about 41 UK tourist

Equipment
- Large-scale maps of area
- Camera

UP TO ONE DAY

beaches holding this award (see Blue Flag website – www.blueflag.org).

'Coastal management', *Geography Review*, vol. 7, no. 2, May 1993.

page 23

Channel Surveys

The measurement of stream or river channels in terms of their size and shape, their flow velocities and discharge levels can yield sound **objective** primary data, particularly with repeat sampling. This allows plenty of scope for analysis and a variety of presentation techniques. Also, it fits in well with **hypothesis** testing (e.g. flow velocity tends to increase in a downstream direction), and allows the use of several statistical techniques, e.g. scatter graphs.

Related areas of study include:

- the bankfull condition, and how this relates to the observed cross-sectional area and discharge levels
- the efficiency of the river in terms of its wetted perimeter and hydraulic radius
- the nature of the river's load and how this relates to changes in channel shape, flow velocities and discharge levels
- the link between meandering and straighter sections in terms of channel depth, flow velocities, turbulence and bedload.

Where to conduct such surveys

There are numerous surface water channels in the British Isles, but only some are suitable for this type of study (and then only limited sections within them). Consider the following, paying particular attention to the safety aspects (see tinted boxes).

7. You need to consider safe parking spots and how far these are from your survey sites.

6. Your chosen section should include some features which could influence flow and discharge levels, e.g. tributary networks and confluences, changes in slope, different land uses (urban, woodland, arable, moorland, etc).

The main decisions

1. The scale of the river – it may be too wide, too deep (>1m) or too fast flowing for safety, or it may be too shallow to allow worthwhile measurements (some rivers dry up during the summer months, right in the middle of the coursework period).

2. The river section under study should not be tidal.

3. Rivers mostly flow across private land – you need to check that your survey points are accessible to the public, easy to get to, and safe (e.g. no cliffs, bulls, dense undergrowth or **'boy racers'** on narrow lanes).

5. Your chosen section should be long enough to allow obvious changes in channel size, discharge levels, sediment load, etc., as you go downstream (say 5-25km).

4. Your chosen section should be close enough to your home to make the study feasible, i.e. within one hour's travel.

Note: The sampling decision will usually be taken by the school, teacher and/or field centre based on the above **factors** and using their local knowledge and experience.

With reference to points 1-7 above, identify the river/stream A-D on Figure 1 that would be most suitable for channel surveying. Justify your decision. Can you spot the deliberate mistake in Figure 1?

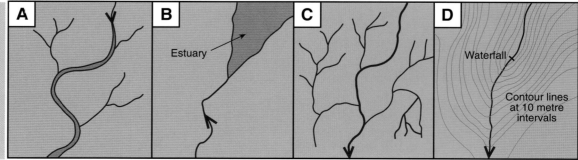

A

B Estuary

C

D Waterfall — Contour lines at 10 metre intervals

Figure 1: Four examples of river/stream systems (as shown on 1:50 000 scale maps).

'The drainage basin – morphometric analysis', *Geography Review*, vol. 6, no. 5, May 1993.

Designing the study

Examiners are impressed by evidence that the student has been through a decision-making process and can justify why other local rivers/streams have been considered and rejected, as well as why they chose a particular section for study. Try the following stepped approach:

Step 1

Get copies of Ordnance Survey 1:50 000 maps (Landranger series), which cover your local area (it may be on more than one map). Lay them out on a large surface and, as a group, decide on a suitable river/stream, bearing in mind points 1-6 opposite. The ideal mix of points may not exist so you could be forced to choose the best of a bad bunch. Note that if a river/stream marked at this map scale is more than just a wiggly blue line, and has both banks marked on (with blue shading in between), it will probably be both too wide and too deep to use.

Step 2

Having selected your river/stream, decide on the channel length that you wish to survey and how many sampling points you will need. Remember that channel measurements should be completed in a single day, so this section should not be too long and the survey points should not exceed eight (allowing about 1 hour per survey point, including transfer time). Consider the hours of daylight available, and the overall distance to be walked. A more detailed map, i.e. Ordnance Survey 1:25 000 Pathfinder or Explorer series), would be helpful.

Step 3

Decide on your sampling strategy (see pages 74-79). Your decision will probably be guided by common sense. Take account of: accessibility, time availability, group size, obvious sampling points (road bridges are useful as the channel beneath them is often uniformly shaped by concrete). You should also decide on your repeat sampling strategy (a burst of heavy rainfall provides an opportunity not to be missed).

Step 4

Do a **pilot survey** to check if your proposed sites are approachable, if you can walk between some of them, if vehicles can be safely parked nearby, and most important of all, if the channel size and speed of flow are suitable for measuring. Also check out the equipment you will be using and anticipate any difficulties relating to its use.

How to do a survey

1. Channel width: use a tape measure staked at the zero end and pulled from the other bank so that it is tight and just above the water level (Figure 3a).

2. Bankfull width: taken at the obvious 'breaks in slope' on both banks – secure a tight string or light rope with stakes at both ends. This line should be horizontal, representing the maximum volume of water that the channel can hold. Measure using a tape (Figure 3a).

3. Channel depth: taken at regular intervals. The wider the channel, the more intervals you should use, to a maximum of 7-8 (e.g. if the channel is 2m wide, divide by 5 to give 4 survey points 0.4m apart). Use a metre ruler to read off depth (Figure 3b). Rest it on the bed, thin side facing upstream.

4. Bankfull depth: the vertical distance between the water level and the line representing the bankfull width – this should not vary across the river (Figure 3a).

5. Flow velocity: ideally use a flowmeter, e.g. hydro-prop with propeller facing upstream at the same points as the depth surveys (Figure 3c). Or you can use a float, e.g. an orange or dog biscuit, and see how long it takes to go a set distance (5-10 m). You can then calculate **mean** velocity by dividing distance by time taken (seconds). Multiply your answer by 0.85 to take into account the line of fastest flow.

6. Wetted perimeter: this is the total distance that the river water is in contact with the bed and banks, at a given cross-section. This is difficult to measure accurately, particularly if the bed is very rough and the river fast flowing. Use a tape measure, rope or chain, starting at the water level on one bank (Figure 3d). Work across the river bed trying to keep the tape/rope/chain in contact with the bed and its bedload at all times. You should start and finish at the same points where channel width was taken.

Figure 3 (right): Measuring (a) channel and bankfull width, (b) channel and bankfull depth, (c) flow velocity, and (d) wetted perimeter.

Figure 2

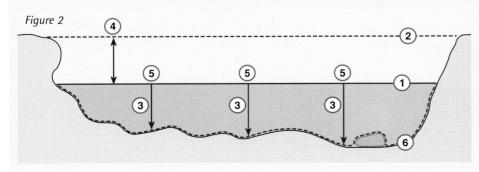

'Measuring upland streams', *Geography Review*, vol. 11, no. 1, September 1997.

page 25

Project title ....

Site no ◯ Name(s) ....

Location .... Day/date/time: ....

1. Channel width = ... 2. Bankfull width = ... 3. Wetted perimeter = ...

4. Channel depth =

5. Mean channel depth = ...

6. Bankfull depth = ...

7. Cross sectional area = channel width(1) x mean depth(5) = ... sq metres

8. Bankfull cross-sectional area = bankful width(2) x mean depth(6) = ... sq metres

9. Hydraulic radius = $\frac{\text{cross-sectional area}^{(7)}}{\text{wetted perimeter}^{(3)}}$ = ...

10. Flow velocity using flowmeter =

conversion formula = ...

mean flow velocity = ... m/s

11. Flow velocity using improvised floats five times for **accuracy**

	A	B	C	D	E
Time (secs)					
Distance (metres)					

mean flow velocity = $\frac{\text{time in seconds}}{\text{distance travelled in metres}}$ x 0.85 = ... m/s

12. Stream discharge = channel width(1) x mean depth(5) x mean flow velocity(10/11) = ☐ cumecs

13. Channel gradient over .... metres = ...%

SITE SKETCH

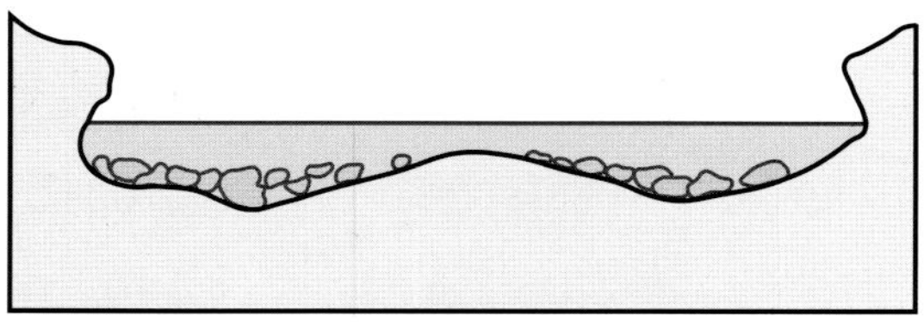

Sectional View

Site comments

Short undercut river cliffs to both sides. Rocky bedload creating turbulent flow. Evidence of attrition and sorting in the bedload. Clear water indicating little silt/clay suspended load.

Figure 4: Recording sheet.

Equipment

UP TO TWO DAYS

- **Large-scale** map(s), recording sheets, clip-board, pencils, calculator
- 20-30m tape, metre ruler, long rope or chain, stakes
- Flowmeter and floats, stopwatch, gradient measuring equipment
- Wellies and/or waders, waterproof clothing, camera
- Disposable plastic gloves

Notes

- Make sure all the units are in metres, with centimetres as decimal points, e.g. with three channel depth measurements of 42, 54 and 24cm, the mean depth is 0.40m.
- With respect to channel depth (Figure 4, item 4), always take the first depth measurement closest to the true left bank (LB) which is on your left as you look downstream. Notice that items 4 and 10 in Figure 4 are in line with each other since these measurements are taken at the same interval points across the channel.
- It is a good idea to highlight the boxed discharge figure as this is the single most important measurement.
- The site comments can include significant channel features (e.g. **pools and riffles**, bank vegetation and slope, water clarity and degree of turbulence, adjacent land use).
- The recording sheet in Figure 4 is only an example. You can modify it depending on your own purpose. Thus, if you are not interested in bankfull conditions, then delete items 2, 6 and 8 and re-number the others. If sediment load is being investigated, then you will need to incorporate this into the recording sheet.

'Investigating river flooding', *Geography Review*, vol. 5, no. 5, May 1992.

Try these

- An unusual approach is to start off with a short section (less than 50m) where the channel is fairly straight, where flow velocities seem relatively steady, and where no tributaries enter. Under these conditions, there should be minimal variation in the discharge figures. The group should make five separate discharge surveys, each about 10m apart. You might be surprised by the variation in your results, revealing the need for **accurate** and repeat sampling and reminding you that the mean depth may be a fairly inaccurate figure (particularly when discharge values are less than 0.1 cumecs). If improvised floats (e.g. dog biscuits, orange peel, cauliflower florets) get snagged, slowed by grounding or marooned in slack water, prod them with a 1m rule to get them going again.

- Specimen sampling can give a valuable insight into the validity of your results. From your five specimen sites, work out the overall range and the **mean** of your discharge figures. If: $\frac{\text{range}}{\text{mean}} \times 100$ is greater than 50% you need to think twice before making any sweeping conclusions about your data gathering. The lower this percentage, the more reliable is your sampling.

Hints and tips

- Channel surveys lend themselves to group work with people having different roles. For example, one person (who can be trusted with a calculator) can be the recorder, another can read off the measurements, the others do the donkey work.

- Always try to stand downstream of where the measurements are being taken, to minimise false readings due to turbulence – particularly velocity readings.

- Photographs can be very useful to illustrate the nature of each site, to show the equipment being used, and to capture the group 'in action' (Figures 3 and 5).

- By using both a flow meter and improvised floats it is possible to comment upon the contrasting velocity figures, and the degree to which they are consistent. In terms of reliability, flow meters are generally more accurate, but not under low flow conditions, so it may be best to use the average values of the two techniques.

- Secondary hydrographic records may be available from the Environment Agency (see page 111) if there is a monitoring station along your stretch of river/stream, or from the work of previous student groups. Field study centres should have a data bank of this type of work, listed by day/month/year.

Bankfull conditions

This is when most erosion and transportation takes place in the channel (refer to Figure 2 for how to measure bankfull width and depth). Bankfull flow velocity measurement/calculations are not really achievable and so it is not possible to derive a figure for bankfull discharge.

The bankfull width-to-depth ratio is useful. If this ratio exceeds 20, then the channel will be increasingly dominated by bedload and may well be **braided**, with gravel beaches and 'islands' (Figure 5). If the ratio is less than 10, then the channel will be deeper and smoother, and so suspended load will dominate.

Channel efficiency

The width-to-depth ratio gives an insight into the efficiency of a channel, i.e. the ability of a river to maintain energy whilst transporting water and sediment. High ratios indicate fairly efficient systems, and vice versa.

$$\text{Hydraulic radius} = \frac{\text{cross sectional area}}{\text{wetted perimeter}}$$

(This is an **index** value – there are no units.)

Figure 6: Channel efficiency.

Figure 5: A braided channel.

'Predicting bankfull flows', *Geography Review*, vol. 3, no. 5, May 1990.

page **27**

Sediment load

Rivers carry three types of load – bedload, suspended load and solution load. The nature of this sediment load will be a **function** of many factors including: flow velocity and discharge levels, channel gradient, width-to-depth ratios, **sinuosity**, local slope processes, geology, etc. In general, the further you go away from a river's source the smaller and more rounded the sediment load becomes.

Bedload

Four techniques for you to consider:

1. A simple approach is to collect bedload samples using the same intervals as for channel depth readings. A stoneboard is useful for this exercise (see page 21).

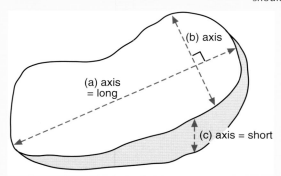

Figure 7: Measuring the axes of pebbles.

- Shut your eyes and pick up 5 to 10 pebbles closest to the base of the metre rule. This selection is not as random as it might appear as you will naturally avoid boulders and you will favour stones, pebbles and cobbles rather than the much smaller gravel and shingle.

- Measure only the (b) axis (Figure 7) since this is the one the pebbles will tend to roll along on the river bed.

- Calculate the mean for each sampling interval and then the overall mean (b axis) for each site.

2. Another approach is to assess stream **competence**.

- Select a fairly straight section of channel with an even bed and minimal obstructions. The water should be fairly clear and shallow.

- Collect a range of reasonably well-rounded pebbles, say 10 from each of the four size categories (Figure 8). You may need to adjust these categories, depending on the energy of the river.

- Colour-code the pebbles according to category by painting them in bright colours (to aid recognition). High-visibility paint in 'tester pots' is ideal for this. It may also help to number each pebble individually and to weigh each one (their degree of roundness should be similar).

- Line up all the pebbles at a marked point across the stream and over the following days/weeks attempt to plot their travel paths downstream, relating this to changes in river energy (flow velocity) and river bed conditions. This is not always as easy as it sounds since some of the pebbles will become lodged on the river bed, and energy conditions will vary across the channel. You will need to experiment – the results may not always be conclusive, but will probably be intriguing.

Equipment

- Metre rule
- Stoneboard, high visibility paint
- Home-made bedload trap

UP TO
TWO
DAYS

3. Measuring the volume of bedload can be tricky. The best way is as shown in Figure 9.

- Dig a shallow trench across the floor of a small stream, 20-30cm wide then make an open wooden box which will sit in the trench just below bed level.

- At given intervals (every 24/48 hours), collect, weigh and measure the trapped contents. Try to relate this data to changes in discharge and flow velocity.

4. If your study includes river beaches (otherwise known as slip-off slopes or **point-bars**), these could surveyed at the same time as bedload. You could map their occurrence, measure their shape and size at varying discharge levels, and make sorting surveys to find out if the gravel and pebbles significantly vary in size in a downstream or downbeach direction, or both.

Figure 9: A bedload trap.

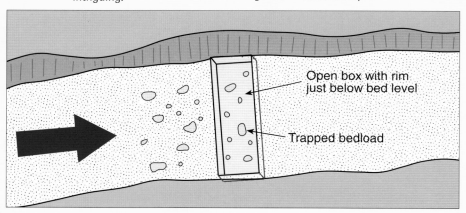

Open box with rim just below bed level

Trapped bedload

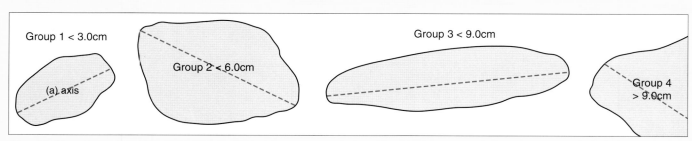

Figure 8: Grouping pebble shapes.

Group 1 < 3.0cm

(a) axis

Group 2 < 6.0cm

Group 3 < 9.0cm

Group 4 > 9.0cm

Suspended load

This involves much smaller material – fine sand particles, silts and clay. The suspended load is generally related to discharge levels, hence the silt-laden and murky nature of large rivers. But suspended load may also vary according to the degree of vegetation cover, slope angles, valley land uses, or the intensity of rainfall/snow melt.

If your chosen river is large enough, and the study section long enough, you should be able to assess changes in suspended sediment concentrations by following these steps:

1. Collect a set of plastic, screw-cap, one-litre containers with wide tops (you will need as many bottles as there are survey sites). Find a cork to fit the top, drill two holes in it and push two flexible tubes into the opening of the bottle (Figure 10).

2. At the first site, anchor the bottle to the river bed with the opening facing upstream (stand downstream to avoid stirring up bed sediment).

3. When the bottle is full, lift it out and remove the cork and tubes. Seal with the original screw cap and label. Repeat the process at other survey sites, using different bottles.

4. At home or school leave the containers to stand overnight to allow sediment settling – comment upon the thickness of sediment layer, its colour, the water clarity and, if possible, the settling rate.

5. Shake the containers so that the sediment is thoroughly re-mixed, then very slowly pour the contents through filter paper of known dry weight – this is a slow process and it can only be done properly with a filter suction pump (your science teacher may need to help you).

6. Dry the filter paper plus sediment in an oven for a couple of hours at around 100°C or gas mark 2-3.

7. Remove and weigh. Subtract the known weight of the dry filter paper to give the weight of the suspended sediment sample.

The suspended sediment concentration can be expressed as grams per litre of river water. If the river discharge is measured in cumecs, then it is possible to estimate the suspended sediment load passing a fixed point on the bank in one second, i.e.:

Suspended sediment concentration	= 0.40 grams per litre
River discharge	= 1.20 cumecs (there are 1000 litres in a cumec)

So, 1200 x 0.40 = 480g suspended sediment. That is about the same as the contents of a ketchup bottle

Solution load

This will vary according to:

Geology: e.g. calcium carbonate from limestone or chalk **catchments**

Discharge: usually higher discharges dilute the soluble load and vice versa.

Effluent levels: these have the effect of increasing the solution load, e.g. chemical discharges from industrial sites.

A conductivity meter is required to measure the solution concentrations in a river. The reading, in micro-siemens, is multiplied by 0.65 to give the approximate concentration in milligrams per litre. This reading includes all the dissolved material. Check with your science teacher to see if this is a starter.

And finally ...

Depending on the nature of your chosen river or stream, you may be able to explore differing aspects of the meandering and straight sections, particularly where well-developed pools and riffles exist. Flow velocities and bedload may be markedly different in these contrasting river environments. It may also be possible to explore the **relationships** between channel depth and width; sinuosity and meander belt width.

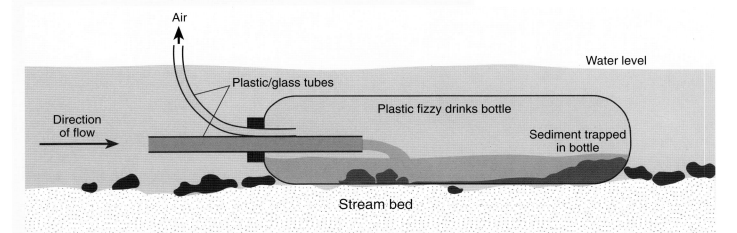

Notes: The larger entry tube is straight, to let water in, while the other tube is curved to let air out.

Remember to anchor the bottle (e.g. with rocks), otherwise it will float away.

Figure 10: A home-made suspended sediment sampler.

Lenon, B. and Cleves, P. (1994) *Fieldwork Techniques in Geography.* Collins Educational, pages 40-45.

Discovery Fieldwork

Rather like the voyages of Columbus this unit is about 'journeys into discovery' – exploring environments in ways that might reveal the unexpected and unusual. By looking, thinking, feeling and sensing in new ways, it is possible to discover things in your surroundings that are either unusual in themselves, or which lead to interesting questions and ideas for further exploration. This 'decouvert' approach first became popular in the 1970s when it was felt that something different from traditional methods was needed to help students to appreciate the rich tapestry of environments around them. The idea is that you, or a group of you, identify what you want to study, and how to go about it. In other words, you are in charge, not the teacher – the aim being to help you to become self-motivating and self-confident.

Mary Evans Picture Library

When to use

There is always a danger with coursework that certain 'popular' environments become over-studied, with the result that both students and teachers become bored with the same old outcomes. There is also the danger that, even if the study area is unfamiliar, the themes chosen for study are lacking in interest or originality.

Here is a simple example: imagine finding a mattress which has been dumped in a countryside park. Most of us would probably walk past it, thinking of it merely as a discarded object that is out of place and an eyesore. But there are other ways of looking at the mattress which might open up some interesting ideas and fresh coursework opportunities:

- What does the discarded mattress suggest about our own perceptions of public open space?

- How and when was the mattress disposed of, and what value did the people involved put on recreational space like the park?

- When the mattress slowly decomposes, it may provide a range of **micro**habitats for insects and mammals as well as providing useful materials (e.g. for making birds' nests).

How to use the discovery approach

The essence of the discovery method is that much of what you do should be spontaneous (Figure 1). However, some key decisions need to be taken before you start, and the following guidelines might help. The first thing to note is that the study area should be small in scale.

Limitations

- 'Discovery' fieldwork may produce outcomes which have very little to do with conventional geographical thinking, thus running the risk of not being acceptable to the Examiner.

- Some people, however hard they try, lack the sensory and observational skills needed to make a success of this fieldwork approach. In other words, they 'look but the don't see'.

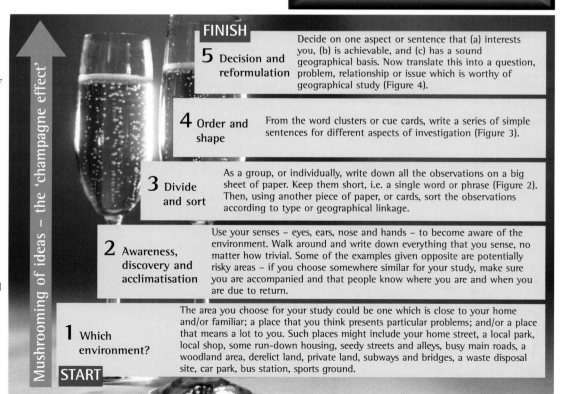

Mushrooming of ideas – the 'champagne effect'

FINISH

5 Decision and reformulation Decide on one aspect or sentence that (a) interests you, (b) is achievable, and (c) has a sound geographical basis. Now translate this into a question, problem, relationship or issue which is worthy of geographical study (Figure 4).

4 Order and shape From the word clusters or cue cards, write a series of simple sentences for different aspects of investigation (Figure 3).

3 Divide and sort As a group, or individually, write down all the observations on a big sheet of paper. Keep them short, i.e. a single word or phrase (Figure 2). Then, using another piece of paper, or cards, sort the observations according to type or geographical linkage.

2 Awareness, discovery and acclimatisation Use your senses – eyes, ears, nose and hands – to become aware of the environment. Walk around and write down everything that you sense, no matter how trivial. Some of the examples given opposite are potentially risky areas – if you choose somewhere similar for your study, make sure you are accompanied and that people know where you are and when you are due to return.

1 Which environment? The area you choose for your study could be one which is close to your home and/or familiar; a place that you think presents particular problems; and/or a place that means a lot to you. Such places might include your home street, a local park, local shop, some run-down housing, seedy streets and alleys, busy main roads, a woodland area, derelict land, private land, subways and bridges, a waste disposal site, car park, bus station, sports ground.

START

Figure 1: The five stages of discovery.

Where to go from here: an example

1: Which environment?

For their coursework, a group of three AS-level Geography students choose to study their local town centre. The town centre is divided into three roughly equal zones, but the pedestrianised high street is common to each.

2: Awareness, discovery and acclimatisation

The group decide to spend one hour in the town centre, recording on clipboards everything that occurs to them.

3: Divide and sort

Their ideas are then sorted and transferred to cards – two examples are given in Figure 3.

Some possible prompts for this study might be:

- Suggest a number of ways in which the area has been improved (e.g. changes to road layout), and a number of ways in which it has been degraded (e.g. empty premises).
- Use words to describe the people around you – tense/calm, silent/talking, worried/carefree, rushed/relaxed, smart/scruffy, ugly/attractive, single/pairs/groups, white/coloured/black, affluent/

Figure 2: Flip chart

Cast-iron bins, concrete, pot plants, traffic, the wind, bus shelter, poor, conversation, street lights, petrol, vehicles, dreadlocks, coffee, happy, wheelie bins, fast cars, burger boxes, crowded pavements, cold, lorries, vomit, dogs, cigarette ends, exhausts, scared, McDonalds, drunk, cheerful, lonely, chewing gum, sandstone, kerbs, perfume, uptight, doorways, arguments, cycling, buskers, busy, dull, weeds, shade, leaves, road sweeper, restless, hope, why?

UP TO HALF A DAY

Homeless

Big Issue, Dogs, Coloured hats, Cold, Poor, Tense, Chatty, Blankets, String, Drink, Space

Pollution and energy

Streetlights, Cars fumes, Lorries, Burger boxes, Paper, Buses, Taxis, Litter, Cigarette ends, Dog litter, Junctions, Double yellow lines, Diesel fumes, Illuminated windows, Cyclists, Concrete, Wind

Figure 3: Cue cards.

poor, ordinary/weird.

- What different building materials are used in the area? Where could they have come from? How well do they blend in?
- If you were homeless, where might you attempt to spend the night?
- What living things can you see from where you are?
- Observe a street for five or ten minutes – write down what is happening and then close your eyes and concentrate on the sounds.
- In what ways is energy being used, and where does it come from?

- What problems might you have in this area if you were: in a wheelchair; a small child; a mother with a pram; or blind?
- What things can you see around you that link the area with other countries?
- What are the obvious smells on the street?
- How would you feel to be in this area, by yourself, late at night?

4: Order and Shape and 5: Decision and reformulation

Enquiry sentence – question, pattern, relationship or issue:	Scale	Achievable	Geographic
1. There are problems due to a lack of suitable and affordable housing.	?	✓	?
2. Environmental quality is surprisingly low in many parts of the town centre.	✓	✓	✓
3. Why do people tend to avoid homeless people on the streets?	✓	✓	✗
4. There is a distance-decay of burger boxes away from McDonalds.	✗	✓	?
5. Air quality is lowest where traffic is congested.	✓	✓	✓
6. Why do town planners not address the problems in urban areas?	?	✗	✓
7. Certain parts of the town centre are lively and vibrant.	✓	✓	?
8. Pedestrian densities are extremely variable in the town centre.	✓	✓	✓

Note: ✗ indicates that this is not a suitable line of enquiry, a ? should not put you off.

Figure 4: Some outcomes of the discovery exercise.

Job, D., Day, C. and Smyth, T. (1999) *Beyond the Bikesheds*. Geographical Association, pages 35-37.

Environmental Impact Assessment

Environmental Impact Assessment (EIA) is the systematic analysis of the likely environmental impacts of a proposed project or development – a type of audit, common in the commercial world, taking into account future costs and benefits. EIA offers challenging avenues for study, especially where people-environment conflict is involved, e.g. the Newbury bypass, extension to Manchester Airport, large housing development on the edge of a village, siting of wind farms in upland areas. EIAs will help you appreciate the range of opinions that can be generated by such issues and develop your empathy skills.

When to use EIA

EIAs are mandatory for major developments such as new transport routes, power stations or coastal protection schemes. The technique is equally valuable for assessing the impact of smaller projects in your local area – for instance, a new supermarket or retail park; a relocated football stadium; an edge-of-town car dealership; an open-cast mine near your home.

Photo: British Wind Energy Association.

Did you know?

- EIA originated in the USA some 30 years ago. Many countries have now established EIA systems which are carried out by government departments or private agencies. Developing nations may be less eager to carry out environmental **audits** because they are lengthy, costly procedures which conflict with their need for rapid industrialisation.

- EIA has become a powerful tool for litigants. In a landmark case in 1998 a quarry developer in Yorkshire had his extraction licence withdrawn because he failed to complete an Environmental Statement.

How to do it

1 **Do your research:** EIA requires an understanding of the proposed project, in particular the range of views it generates, so get some background information on local issues, e.g. newspaper articles, planning applications.

2 **Collect baseline data:** Collect primary data describing the original condition of the site.

3 **Describe the project:** Your description should include the nature and scale of the project, the time frame of the construction and its likely environmental impact – use the Impact checklist for this, adapting it to your own particular study.

4 **Draw up an impact matrix** (see opposite).

5 Now you have an overview of the proposal, you can identify alternatives and propose modifications – there may be other ways of achieving the same objectives. This may involve drawing up your own management plan, and this should include justifications for your main decisions.

6 **Analyse the options** There may be ways to reduce the environmental impact, e.g. pollution control, nature conservation, transport strategies.

7 Now prepare your draft environmental statement. This should list the short and long-term effects of the project and propose the best alternatives. You should communicate your findings in non-technical language that the ordinary person can understand.

An **Environmental Impact Assessment** is designed to identify and communicate information about a development and predict its impact.

An **Environmental Statement** lists the possible, probable or certain impacts on the environment of a proposed development.

Impact checklist

Ecological (including pollution)
Effects on air, water, noise levels, flora, fauna, species **diversity**, historical and cultural heritage, visual environment, soil erosion and land degradation

Natural resources
Effects on agricultural land, forests, water supplies, mineral resources, wetlands and other areas of wilderness or **wildscape**

Social
Effects on settlement patterns, land use, housing, social quality, recreational activities and **amenities**, community services

Economic
Effects on employment opportunities, access to services and facilities, urban infrastructure, prices of goods and services and land prices

ICT links

Using programs like *Landscape Explorer* and *Vistapro*, it is possible to generate a **rendered** GIS image of the landscape. This allows you to 'see' the impact of a proposed development.

'Environmental Impact Assessment in the 1990s', *Geofile*, no. 240, April 1994.

Impact matrix

Impact matrices show interactions between environmental factors and project characteristics.

You may have to devise two matrices – one for the construction phase (see Figure 1) and one for the operational phase.

1 Make a simplified list of activities that characterise the project, e.g. increased traffic.

2 List the environmental factors, e.g. air quality.

3 Arrange these lists into a grid or matrix (Figure 1) with project characteristics along the top and environmental factors down the side.

4 Taking each project characteristic in turn, consider its impact on the environmental factors and complete the matrix using the following system:

    no impact: score 0
    low impact: score 1
    moderate impact: score 2
    severe impact: score 3

If the impact of a characteristic is difficult to categorise you can use split values, e.g. low to medium impact scores 1.5.

5 You can take the matrix a step further by **weighting** the most significant environmental **factors**. For instance, if the river to be dammed is a major element of the regional economy you multiply the impact score of the dam construction by 2 to give an impact score of 6 (see red cell in matrix). Conversely, there may be few local people living near this upland site, so divide the workforce impact score by two to give an impact score of 1 (see blue cell in matrix).

6 Total the rows and columns in the matrix to give the overall impact scores.

Note: The outcomes will be both interesting and revealing, but remember that projects like dams, bypasses and retail parks have both immediate and long-term environmental impacts. You may find it difficult to assess long-term impacts within the scope of your coursework, so the outcomes may not be conclusive.

Environmental factors	traffic issues	raw materials	additional buildings	workforce	waste disposal	reservoir/ water supply	landscaping	Total environmental factors
flora	1	2	1	0	1	1	3	9
fauna	1	2	2	0	1	1	3	10
hydrological characteristics	0	1	6	0	1	1	3	12
local microclimate	0	0	1	0	0	0	0	1
landscape/intrinsic appeal	2	2	1	1	2	1	3	12
tourism resource	2	3	2	1	2	0	1.5	11.5
noise	2.5	0	0	2	0	0	3	7.5
air quality	0	1	0	0	0	0	1	2
local residents	3	2	1	1	2	1	1	11
landowners	1	1	1	0	1	0	1	5
Total Project Characteristics	12.5	14	15	5	10	5	19.5	

(Column group header: Project characteristics)

Figure 1: Impact matrix for the constructional phase of a proposed upland reservoir.

Figure 2: A hill valley in the UK, and how it could look with a dam in it.

Gilpin, A. (1995) *Environmental Impact Assessment – Cutting edge for the 21st century.* Cambridge University Press.

Field Sketching

The essence of all fieldwork is to observe, record and interpret what you see around you. Field sketching is a vital part of that process, even if you think you are useless at it – have a go. Field sketching helps you to look closely at the inter-related elements of an environment to decide which are more important than others. You may also gain an insight into how the environment has evolved. It is a qualitative technique which involves very little effort, equipment or even skill - provided you keep it simple. Also useful for interpretative work are sketches based on 'virtual' landscapes and scenes, such as photographs or paintings.

Limitations

- Sketching is a non-starter under adverse weather conditions (rain, wind and cold).
- Many geography students have a negative attitude towards field sketches and typically dash them off in a few minutes. (Are you one of them?

Hints and tips

- Use a clipboard/stiff notebook to rest your sketch paper on.
- Use as large a piece of paper as possible so that there is plenty of room for labelling. Draw a border or frame to give shape to the area you want to show.
- Use a soft pencil and make sure you have a rubber handy.
- Number your sketch and give it a good working title which clearly locates it. Using a place name and a grid reference is ideal.
- Decide on your priorities, and ignore unnecessary detail (e.g. sheep or cars might not be relevant to the purpose of the sketch).
- Write on the sketch the direction of view using either compass directions, bearings and/or a written description (e.g. 'Looking down High Street towards West Street').
- It is helpful to convey a sense of scale, even though the depth of field will distort this (trees and buildings help to do this, and if you know the actual heights of hills, etc., these can be added (see Figure 2).
- Landscape drawing: When drawing slopes, be careful not to make them too steep. Hold the pencil at arm's length to gauge the correct angle, then transfer this to the paper.

Photo: Steve Day.

ICT links

If you have access to a digital camera, you could use it to photograph the study area, and add labels using a computer. Or you could use the camera to photograph your field sketch, then 'improve' or alter it on the computer.

How to do it

Find a safe, comfortable and sheltered position to make the sketch.

Before you start, think carefully about the main purpose and value of the sketch you will make. This will help you to decide on your priorities - what to include, and what to make prominent.

Orientate the paper to sketch the view and maximise the paper space available.

If the view you intend to sketch includes sky and a horizon, divide your paper roughly into three parts: one for the horizon and sky, one for the middle-ground, and one for the foreground (Figure 1a).

Equipment

- Clipboard/notebook with stiff back
- Soft pencil and rubber
- Plain paper
- Camera

LESS THAN ONE HOUR

Make a frame on the paper and start by drawing the things that are furthest away from you, working towards the foreground (Figure 1b).

Label the main elements of the sketch (keeping its main purpose in mind) and put a number beside each key feature (Figure 2). These numbers can be referred to in written commentaries (annotations) about the scene.

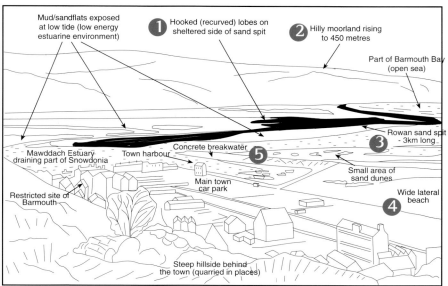

Figure 2: The field sketch complete with annotations.

In Figure 2, the following annotations appear:

Mud/sandflats exposed at low tide (low energy estuarine environment)

1 Hooked (recurved) lobes on sheltered side of sand spit

2 Hilly moorland rising to 450 metres

Part of Barmouth Bay (open sea)

Rowan sand spit - 3km long

Mawddach Estuary draining part of Snowdonia

Town harbour

Concrete breakwater

5

Small area of sand dunes

Main town car park

Wide lateral beach

4

3

Restricted site of Barmouth

Steep hillside behind the town (quarried in places)

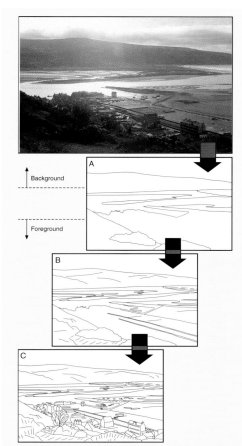

Background

Foreground

A

B

C

Figure 1: The construction of a field sketch of a view of Barmouth.

Ways of using sketches

- If you have old photographs or paintings of the view you have sketched, you can compare them to note changes over time and the causes and consequences of those changes (see Figures 3 and 4).

- Using the numbered/labelled items on your sketch, you can write an analytical commentary of what it shows, focusing on processes and issues. When sketches are analysed effectively and referred to appropriately they enhance the whole report or study.

- By comparing sketches made by different people of the same scene, you may discover some interesting things about how and why people have different perceptions. For example, they may be influenced by what they already know about the area, and by their knowledge of the processes that have affected it. Age, gender, culture and general background may also be influential factors.

South Hallsands on the South Devon coast was once a thriving fishing village of about 100 people. The photograph shows that in 1894 the village consisted of two rows of houses built on a rock platform; in front was a 50m-wide shingle beach on which fishing boats were drawn up. However, between 1897 and 1900 nearly half a million cubic metres of shingle was dredged from a nearby offshore bar for the extension of the naval dockyard at Plymouth. This dredging created a void in the inshore sediment transport system, resulting in the 'sucking-in' of material from adjacent beaches to replenish the depleted offshore shingle bank. This left the beach and rock platform at Hallsands vulnerable to erosion, particularly from easterly winter storms. In January 1917 a major storm event overwhelmed the village, undermining the rock platform, eroding the sediment-filled crevices within it, and causing the collapse of nearly half of the 25 dwellings. The village was abandoned that night, save for one house, never to be permanently lived in again.

In Figure 3, the following annotations appear:

Steep vegetated coastal cliffs

Narrow confined site

Entrance pathway, now closed to public

The London Inn was once here

Ruins of part of the original back row of houses

Part of Start Bay

Rock platform 6-8m high, 20m wide

'lost' beach

Boulder filled crevice

Figure 3: Field sketch of South Hallsands in 1980.

Figure 4: South Hallsands in 1894. Photo: Cookworthy Museum, Kingsbridge.

'Photographs and field sketches in coursework', *Geography Review*, vol. 12, no. 3, January 1999.

Gradient/Slope Surveys

The Earth's land surface is made up of a mosaic of slopes. They are the building blocks of landforms and as such they are worthy of investigation. The way that the ground slopes depends largely on the rock it is made of, and the tectonic or crustal activity that has affected it. It also depends on how the land has been shaped by **weathering** and erosion (e.g. by rivers, ice, the sea and wind) and modified by human activity (e.g. terracing, ditching, quarrying).

The steepness, or gradient, of slopes is one of the main determinants of how the land is used (Figures 1 and 2). Generally, the steeper the slope the less it can be used for economic activity (Figure 1), though some leisure activities such as rock climbing, hang gliding and skiing actually depend on steepness.

Slope (°)	Gradient example	Steepness	Comment
35-45°	1 in 1	Very steep	Hands needed to scramble up.
20-35°	1 in 2 (50%)	Steep	Roads, tracks and paths zigzag to cope with the slope.
12-20°	1 in 3 (33%)	Fairly steep	Limit for ploughable land and a problem for heavy vehicles on roads.
6-12°	1 in 10 (10%)	Moderate	You will 'feel' this when walking.
3°-6°	1 in 20 (5%)	Gentle	Allow good drainage so OK for building and agriculture.
1°-3°	1 in 60 (1.7%)	Flat	Ideal for railways and most other uses, but may need to be drained in some cases.
<1°	-	Level	Snooker tables.

Figure 1: Classifications for gradients.

Gradient

Slopes are measured in degrees, from 0°-90°, while the gradient of a slope is expressed either as a percentage (as on road signs on hills), or as a ratio.

- To convert degrees of slope to gradient, use the tangent key on your calculator. For example: tan (20°)= 0.364 = 36%.

- To express the gradient as a ratio, use the reciprocal of the tangent. For example: $\frac{1}{0.364}$ = 2.7 so the gradient ratio is 1:2.7

Gradient of 1:2.7 or 36%

Hill road

Varieties of slope

As Figures 2 and 3 show, slopes can be characterised according to their shapes and steepness, with different names used to describe the various types. Typically, a slope profile is made up of different segments separated from each other by breaks of slope where the angle changes, often abruptly.

Why measure slopes?

As well as being interested in the processes that create and form slopes, geographers are also interested in the **relationship** between the angle, height and **aspect** of slopes and such things as vegetation cover and type, soil depth and moisture content, and the ways in which the land can be used.

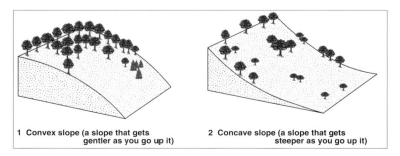

1 Convex slope (a slope that gets gentler as you go up it)

2 Concave slope (a slope that gets steeper as you go up it)

Figure 2: Main slope types.

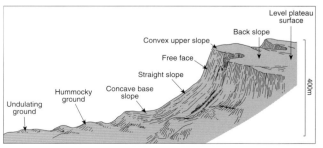

Figure 3: A composite of slopes.

Hints and tips

- The gradient of many slopes (such as the lower sections of rivers) may be so shallow that it is not possible to measure accurately, particularly when it is less than 2°. Try to guess the gradient before you survey it. Most people wildly over-estimate, by a factor of 2 at least. Why do you think this is?

- When field sketching (see pages 34-35) or photographing (see pages 60-61) a slope profile try to find the best vantage point which shows it clearly (from the side!).

- If the vertical rise or fall in each slope segment is greater than the height of the ranging poles, then you will need intermediate survey points.

- Gradients can sometimes be calculated using secondary sources, i.e. by using contours on OS maps of appropriate scales such as 1:25 000 or even 1:10 000. It is interesting to compare map-based calculations with field results (see 'OS Map Skills' pages 56-59).

- It is a good idea to do a practice survey, possibly in the grounds or fields of your school/college. Surveying is generally a three-person job: one on each ranging pole and one to measure/record.

River channel surveys

Surveying the gradient of a river channel is often done at the same time as making other measurements (see pages 24-27). Hold upright ranging poles at equal distances downstream and upstream from the site where the channel width was measured (Figure 5). The further apart they are the better, but they must be inter-visible. Straight sections of channel are not required. Push the metal pointed ends of the poles into the river bed so they are flush with it, or rest them on convenient stones/boulders at water level. The downstream person uses a clinometer to read off the channel slope in degrees. This can then be related to flow velocity, bed load size, or hydraulic radius to see if there is a meaningful connection.

Equipment
- Ranging poles, tape measure, clinometer
- Recording sheets

How to measure slopes

- The height at various points along a slope can be read off Ordnance Survey maps provided there are clear points of reference that can be identified on the ground (e.g. streams, roads, edges of woodland, buildings, trig points).

- To determine the aspect of a slope (the direction in which it faces), use a compass.

- Very simple surveying exercises can be done using a clinometer (including cheap gun clinometers). For example, the heights of trees, buildings and other tall objects can be measured as follows:

  a. measure the horizontal distance to the base of the object,
  b. read off the slope angle in degrees,
  c. apply the tangent calculation described in point 5 in the text below.

- To measure slope profiles and gradients using more sophisticated techniques, see

Figures 4 and 5, and follow the sequence of points below. This involves the technique of levelling along a **transect** line on a regular or systematic basis (say every 5m up a 50m beach), or, more appropriately, on a stratified basis at each significant '**break in slope**'. Points 1-6 below explain how to do it, and Figure 6 shows how to record the results.

1. Decide upon the line of transect – it's overall length and orientation (it should run up the main slope). Mark a start point with something visible and fixed, ideally at a known height. The end point of the transect should be in line with an obvious feature that allows you to keep 'on transect'.

2. Hold a ranging pole upright at either end of the first slope segment. If poles are not available, use two people instead. They must stand upright and their eye levels should be similar.

3. Measure and record the horizontal

distance in metres between the two poles or people (distance Z on Figure 4).

4. Sight a clinometer from a fixed height on the first pole (at the top red/white junction) to the same level on the distant pole. Or sight from eye level to eye level. Read off and record the slope angle (angle x° on Figure 4).

5. Repeat this process, changing the poles over with each slope segment until the slope profile has been surveyed. To calculate the height gained or lost (length 'y' on Figure 4), for each segment use the tangent key on your calculator, as follows:

If the observed angle = 20° and the horizontal distance = 4.70m, then
$$\tan 20° = \frac{y}{4.70}$$
So y = 4.70 x 0.364 = 1.71m

To work out the overall height difference from A to B, add the segment heights together.

6. Using a suitable scale for both the horizontal and vertical axes, plot the results on to graph paper to reconstruct the slope profile.

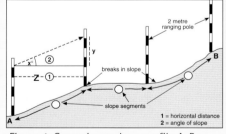

Figure 4: Surveying a slope profile A-B.

Figure 5: Surveying a river channel.

SLOPE RECORDING SHEET   Project title 'Is there a **relationship** between slope angle and scree size beneath various rock outcrops in South Shropshire?'

Location _____   Date _____   Transect Length _____   Name(s) _____

Segment/ Site no.	Start height (m)	Horizontal distance (m)	Slope angle (°)	Height +/- difference	Slope shape	Slope aspect	Comments
1	285	21.0	27	?	Fairly uniform	NE	Very angular scree. Larger boulders towards the base. Little
2							vegetation indicating active ongoing movement of scree.

Figure 6: A slope recording sheet.

Lenon, B. and Cleves, P. (1994) *Fieldwork Techniques in Geography*. Collins Educational, pages 19-20, 40, 50.

Hydrological Investigations

Fresh water is essential for life: not only for people to drink, cook and wash with, but also to maintain the Earth's **ecosystems** and delicate **biosphere**. Hydrology is the study of water: where it comes from and how it is used and stored. Most aspects of hydrology are of interest to geographers, ranging from the study of water inputs to **catchment areas** (i.e. precipitation), to investigations of the pathways that are followed by water (e.g. streams, soil, drains). Central to the study of hydrology is the concept of the **hydrological** cycle (Figure 1). This is too complex to form the basis of a coursework topic in itself, but various aspects of the cycle make ideal subjects for investigation.

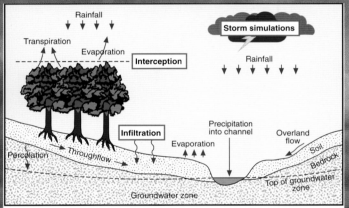

Figure 1: The hydrological cycle. (Possible fieldwork experiments are shown in boxes).

Photo: Robert Grandfield

Suggested projects

Hydrological studies are many and varied and can be carried out in a range of environments: urban and rural, at home or in the school/college grounds. An important advantage is that they have not been 'done to death' in coursework, so there is scope for some fresh projects.

Some examples of topics for study:

- infiltration rates on different soil types and for different surfaces, e.g. bare ground or vegetation cover
- evaporation rates from different surfaces and at different times of the day, or under different weather conditions
- overland flow rates on different angles of slope
- stem flow rates of trees at various times of the year, i.e. spring and autumn
- interception rates of various species of tree in a local woodland.

You can also do simulation exercises, such as the 'storm simulation'.

Hints and tips

- Choose a project that is manageable and set clear limits to the investigation (the inter-relatedness of different aspects of hydrology means that it is often hard to know where to stop). Keep it local in scale.

- You can combine this type of study with other investigations, e.g. **micro**-climate.

- Most local hydrological projects require only simple and straightforward equipment which, if not available in your school/college, can generally be made out of low-cost materials.

- Familiarise yourself with specialist hydrological terms, starting with those in Figure 1 and using a geographical dictionary or other reference source.

- Check what secondary data is available. For example, the Met Office may hold daily records of potential evapo-transpiration (PE) and **humidity** for your area (though it can be expensive to obtain these). Other useful sources are Environment Agency offices or Water Companies (see Contacts, page 111).

'Real world' relevance

The experiments described on these pages provide data which may have relevance to a number of 'real world' situations, as follows:

1. Infiltration experiments: arable farming (issues of soil erosion and gullying in saturated conditions); maintenance of sports fields (some pitches drain better than others); value of land for cultivation.

2. Storm simulations: planning for the consequences of heavy rain falling on different types of surface (e.g. hard surfaces such as tarmac and compacted soils encourage 'flashy' runoff which may result in flooding).

3. Stemflow experiments: trees 'naturally' control rates of water transfer through interception – the volume of transfer varies with the season and the type, age and density of the trees, and can involve significant amounts of water. Large-scale deforestation may have dramatic consequences.

'Measuring infiltration capacity', *Geography Review*, vol. 1, no. 2, November 1987.

Equipment

- Plastic drain pipe
- Plastic ruler
- Stopwatch
- Recording sheet

Infiltration experiments

Infiltration is the passage of water into the soil: the process operates by gravity and capillary action. Normally, infiltration rates are highest at the start of a rainstorm, but decrease as the ground becomes more saturated.

Different surfaces will have very different infiltration rates. You could investigate:

- different soil types (e.g. in your garden, a park or playing fields);
- places with differing vegetation cover;
- footpaths and other routeways with different surfaces;
- any of the above at different times of the day, or before and after rainfall.

Steps to take

1. Make the infiltration tube from a strong 30cm length of plastic drainpipe of standard 10cm diameter. Hammer it into the ground (use a piece of wood on top to prevent the plastic breaking), ensuring there is a good seal with the ground (Figure 2).

2. Pour water in to the tube and measure the rate at which it infiltrates in millimetres per minute. It is important to maintain a constant 'head' of water above the soil, so regular top-ups are required.

3. Record the results and construct your own infiltration graph with time in seconds on the x axis and the vertical drop of the water level in millimetres on the y axis.

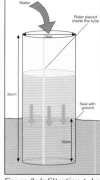

Figure 2: Infiltration tube.

Equipment

To construct the 'cloud' and 'channel' you will need plastic guttering, some wood and a plastic flap
- Several measuring cylinders/jugs
- Stopwatch
- Recording sheet

A storm simulation

This is an experiment for simulating rainfall events over different surfaces, e.g. ploughed fields (bare soil surface), compacted or hard surfaces, and different types of soil. The surfaces can be varied and comparisons made.

Steps to take

Most of the equipment in Figure 3 can be bought at hardware or DIY stores.

1. Steadily pour 5 litres of water into the 'cloud' and time how long it takes for this to get to the lower channel (Initial Response Time). Log this on a record sheet (Figure 4)

2. Collect the run-off every 30 seconds and record the amount (Figure 4). You can also record peak discharge and total discharge.

3. As in Figure 4, repeat this experiment at the same site to simulate successive storm events (allow 10-15 minutes between each).

Note: make sure you keep the slope angle constant.

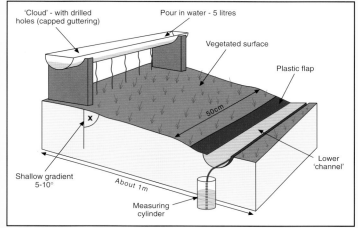

Figure 3: Storm simulation.

Time (seconds)	Discharge (ml)			
	Storm 1	Storm 2	Storm 3	Storm 4
30				
60				
90				
120				

Figure 4: Part of a storm simulation recording sheet.

Limitations

1. It may be difficult to isolate any one single **factor**, e.g. when measuring infiltration rates, the soil type will not be the only **variable** – these rates may be influenced by slope, antecedent rainfall, bedrock and vegetation cover.

2. In reality, no matter how good the survey equipment is, your results may not be scientifically convincing, i.e. repeat sampling, even under similar conditions, may yield surprisingly different results.

Stemflow experiment

The term 'stemflow' means the flow of water down the trunk of a tree. A simple way of measuring this is as follows:

- Tightly wrap a length of flexible tubing (e.g. as in home-brew kit material) around the trunk. Use mastic at the edges to make a good seal (it is easiest if the bark is smooth).

- Make an escape hole in the tubing so that water draining down the trunk can be collected in a measuring cylinder over a number of days (Figure 5).

Equipment

- Flexible tubing
- Mastic
- Measuring cylinder

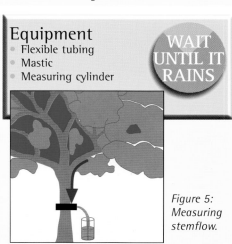

Figure 5: Measuring stemflow.

Interview Surveys

Conducting face-to-face interviews is a very useful way of collecting data that is not available from any other source. In particular, it is invaluable as means of finding out about people's values and their attitudes towards specific local issues. Interviewing is a skill, and needs a little practice. You must be clear about what information you need from your interviews, otherwise you may find yourself getting overloaded with irrelevant detail. You also need to be aware of pitfalls, such as the possibility of upsetting people when asking sensitive or controversial questions.

Limitations

- Be prepared for refusals, either to be interviewed, or to answer more searching questions.

- It is difficult to carry out **quantitative** analysis of the results from an interview.

Hints and tips

- Take advantage of any contacts you have with potential interviewees (e.g. your parents, relatives, school and friends may know useful people).

- Send any letters well in advance of your deadline, bearing in mind that some people have tight schedules and need to plan ahead. Don't overlook your coursework completion dates!

- Think carefully about the sequencing of your questions and the 'tone' they create. You should always test them out on family and/or friends and gauge their reactions (a good simulation exercise).

- Ensure that the questions are unambiguous, open-ended and cannot be answered with a straight 'Yes' or 'No' (see Figure 2).

- Remember to take a pen and notebook (or response form) to the interview. A dictaphone can be very useful too, but only use it if you have prior written permission (many interviewees will refuse this).

- Dress respectfully, act politely and don't outstay your welcome (30 minutes is the maximum time you should allow).

When to use

Most investigations which relate to human activities will benefit from information collected through interviews. This type of 'evidence' adds weight to coursework and reports. Thus, if you are investigating a planning issue, it may be useful to collect opinions from relevant decision makers and others who may be affected by it (e.g. the development manager of a local supermarket which is planning to extend its premises; a local authority planning officer; a town councillor; local residents). Similarly, for a study on visitor behaviour in a National Park, you would expect to obtain useful data from a Park Warden, as well as visitors, local farmers, etc.

Interviews versus questionnaires

Interviews have an advantage over questionnaires in that they give you more flexibility: the questions you ask can be longer, less structured, more detailed, and open-ended. Also, interviews allow people to express their feelings and opinions; they are not making 'forced choices' in categories you have constructed. Finally, in an interview you can follow up points of particular interest with further questions, and you may learn something unexpected which adds substance to your study.

How to do it

General

- Research the background facts to the issue so that you are well briefed.

- Decide exactly who you want to interview and what specific information you want from them. If it is a particular person in an organisation (e.g. a company manager), try to get their name.

- If you are conducting door-to-door or on-the-street surveys, you must decide on a sampling strategy before you start (i.e. how often and how many). Remember – interviews are time consuming, so don't try and do too many.

Interviews with particular people

1. If you plan to interview particular people, write to them beforehand. Your letter must be concise and polite, and should explain clearly who you are, what it is that you are investigating, and why you wish to interview them. Remember to give an address and phone number for your home as well as for a school/college contact person (Figure 1).

2. Wait a week or two for a reply to your letter. If the person agrees to the interview, you need to finalise the place, time and date of the interview. If you get no response to your letter, make a follow-up phone call, and if that fails as well, choose another candidate for interview and start again.

3. The interviewee may ask you to send some specimen questions so you need to be prepared for this. About six questions will do (Figure 2).

Presenting the evidence gained from interviews

- Include your introductory letter and possibly the interviewee's response (in the data collection section).

- You could write out the various elements of the interview process and colour-code them, as follows: 1. your question (e.g. in black), 2. the interviewee's response (e.g. in blue), 3. your comments/analysis (e.g. in red). It seldom works to include the whole interview; be selective but fair.

- A visual presentation can be very effective. For example, you could use photographs to 'set the scene' for the issue or topic under study, or 'talking heads' to represent the range of values and attitudes surrounding the issue.

- Relevant quotes from interviews can add interest and depth to a project, but you need the interviewees' permission to include these.

Equipment

- Notebook and pen, a dictaphone (optional)
- Smart clothes
- Identity badge or letter from school

LESS THAN ONE HOUR

Figure 1: Example of a letter to set up an interview with a key person.

Ms Amy Product
Development Manager
The Medium Supermarket
Co. Ltd
Hertsville
Wessex RN20 1HW

14 Swan Lane, Hertsville
Wessex RN12 4FP
e-mail: phil.chief@hotmail.com

20 April 2000

Dear Ms Amy Product,

I am an A-level Geography student at Hertsville School. As part of my course I am required to undertake an investigative report. I have chosen to study the likely impacts of the planned expansion of the Medium Supermarket Company Ltd. in Hertsville. I would very much like to talk to you, for about 20 minutes, with respect to this. If you wish, I can supply you with a set of prepared questions for your consideration beforehand.

I attach a list of dates when I am available in the summer, plus contact details for myself and for my supervisor at school.

I do hope you will be able to help, and look forward to hearing from you.

Yours sincerely

Phil Chief

Explain who you are first, and what you want.

It is good practice to suggest that you can supply specimen questions

It is important to include dates for when you are able to conduct the interview.

---

1. How many new full-time equivalent jobs do you expect the planned expansion to create?

2. a) Did you do a survey of local residents to seek their opinions on the planned expansion, and if so, who conducted the survey?
   b) How many local residents responded to the survey(s)?
   c) What proportion of respondents to your survey were for and against your plans? What kinds of things did they say in favour and against?
   d) In what way have these opinions influenced your plans?

3 Did your Company commission a detailed environmental impact survey (EIA), and if so could you please summarise the outcomes of this or explain why you did not.

4. In what ways do you expect this development to influence current retail patterns in Hertsville and beyond?

5. What promotional strategies might you be using to attract new customers?

6. In what ways (if any) will you make your enlarged superstore more responsive to customer needs, particularly for disadvantaged groups within the local community?

Figure 2: A specimen set of interview questions.

Notes

- None of the questions in Figure 2 can be 'blocked' with a straight Yes or No response, and the meaning of all of them is clear.

- The questions were carefully selected to give an idea of the intended direction and tone of the full interview.

- The questions follow a sequence, starting with those that require simple, factual answers and progressing towards ones that are more searching. (Note that question 5 is tactical – the answer is simple and easy to provide, and gives the interviewee an opportunity to shine, and feel at ease.)

Judgement Surveys

It is the nature of human species to have attitudes and opinions, and to make judgements. On some occasions this will be based on wide-ranging, impartial and detailed information, supported by experience, understanding and a clear mind. In most cases, however, judgements are made and held on the flimsiest of bases, often leading to **stereotypical** misconceptions, e.g. quarries are commonly perceived as landscape 'eyesores'. Your geography coursework will inevitably involve making judgements, particularly during the evaluation and conclusion. If you use techniques such as conflict matrices, environmental assessments and quality surveys you will be making judgements without even realising it.

Value judgements

Decisions are often arrived at by measuring the worth or value of something. In many cases it is possible to quantify things in monetary terms: for example, the loss of a human limb in an accident might be measured in terms of the financial compensation that the person receives. In other less tangible cases, it may be impossible to place a monetary value on something (e.g. you cannot 'cost' the quality of a view), but it may still be possible to place a numerical value in these cases (see, for example, Figures 1, 3 and 5).

Perception surveys

Such surveys can be the focal point of a study, or – as is mostly the case – used to provide supporting evidence for various lines of enquiry. 'Perceiving' may be defined as 'observing in a sensitive, careful and thoughtful manner', but our perceptions are subjective and **variable** (e.g. eye-witnesses to a road accident seldom agree about the details because of such things as memory lapses and differences due to their relative locations at the time).

The way we perceive things is influenced by a host of **factors**, some more significant than others:

- age
- gender
- cultural background
- past experiences
- family upbringing
- personality
- education
- **peer group** influences
- chance elements (e.g. how you feel at the time).

Perception surveys often involve quality assessment, i.e. an assessment of the quality of an area, service or facility using a mix of **criteria**. All too often this results in crude, simplistic and unconvincing conclusions, but you can minimise this happening if you follow some basic guidelines:

1. Devise a mix of criteria that together represent a reasonably fair way of measuring whatever you are interested in (e.g. in Figure 6 in 'Urban enquiries' (page 91), seven criteria have been used to measure **deprivation**. You will notice that these cover a wide range of **socio-economic** factors – employment, family structure, mobility, health).

2. Some criteria are more important than others and should be **weighted** to reflect their importance. For example, in the example quoted above, unemployment rates have a direct bearing on levels of deprivation, and so the **ranked** position should possibly be doubled or trebled.

3. Try to be as **objective** as possible when devising and scoring criteria; put your own prejudices and beliefs to one side. It will help if you (i) work in a group which is mixed in terms of gender and cultural background, and (ii) discuss your scoring differences and the reasons for them.

4. Give written examples (known as descriptors) for the 'polar' values on a scale. Thus, in an assessment of garden quality as part of a residential survey, if your scale is 0-5 you might describe 0 as meaning 'a neglected, overgrown rubbish tip'. If possible, do the same for the intermediate points on your scale – this will demonstrate greater confidence and conviction and thus add value to your study (e.g. the descriptor for category 3 gardens might be 'reasonably maintained, not detracting from the overall environmental quality'). Remember that each score represents an average impression – you should comment if there is a wide variation within your study area and suggest reasons for it.

Residential environmental assessment

This type of assessment is commonly used to compare different areas within a town or city. It is unwise to base your perception scores on a single street – try to sample a representative range within each residential area. Figure 3 shows a typical approach, using four major categories, each with 2/3 criteria, and employing a bi-polar scoring scale. Some comments have been included for guidance. You can modify the criteria to suit your own study, and also after conducting a **pilot survey**.

Figure 3: Perceptions of an urban area, including bi-polar analysis.

Landscape evaluation

LESS THAN ONE HOUR

If your project involves assessing the impact of changes to the environment (e.g. redevelopment of a **brownfield site**), then by using 'before' and 'after' photographs you can assess a **respondent's** gut reaction by using the type of scoring system shown in Figure 1.

Variations on this theme include:

* assessing the same environmental change but with photographs taken from different camera viewpoints;

* comparing photographs of different types of rural and urban landscapes (see Figure 2).

Different types of people will have very different perspectives and preferences depending upon such things as their age, gender, culture and area of residence. The 'eyes' of a tourist, a local person, a teenager, an unemployed person will see different qualities in the same photograph; what appeals to one group may well be off-putting to another, e.g. one person's idea of tranquillity is another person's social desert.

Figure 2: Sites in (a) a rural area, and (b) an urban area.

Figure 1: Gut feelings using adjectival pairs.

a	boring	1 2 3 ④ 5	stimulating
b	ugly	1 ② 3 4 5	attractive
c	crowded	1 2 3 4 5	peaceful
d	threatening	① 2 3 4 5	welcoming
e	private	① 2 3 4 5	public
f	cold/wet	① 2 3 4 5	warm/dry
g	monotonous	1 ② 3 4 5	varied
h	obvious	1 2 3 ④ 5	mysterious
i	drab	1 2 3 ④ 5	colourful
j	weak	1 2 3 4 ⑤	strong
k	confining	1 2 3 ④ 5	spacious
l	lonely	① 2 3 4 5	sociable
m	modern	1 2 3 4 5	historic

* The idea is that respondents circle the number which most closely reflects their gut feelings with respect to the 'polar' adjectives.

* As in Figure 1, some categories may not apply so can be excluded. You can also invent different ones of your own.

* The left-hand side of these pairings is not necessarily a negative judgement and vice-versa (e.g. modern v historic). However, some of these pairings are clearly value judgements (e.g. ugly v attractive).

Q: The circles marked on Figure 1 show one person's evaluation of the scene shown in Figure 2a. To what extent do you agree with them?

Figure 3

Category/Criteria	Bi-polar score							Justification/comments
	+3	+2	+1	0	-1	-2	-3	
Houses – built environment								
a Quality of external upkeep – walls, doors, paintwork, windows, gutters				✓				Some older villa properties are multi-occupancy and showing signs of wood-rot and paint flaking
b Variety and attractiveness of house designs and materials		✓						Pleasing mix of late Victorian and Edwardian properties, but with a 'hard' brick exterior
Gardens – green environment								
c Proportion and variety of green space – grass, bushes, plants, trees, pots/tubs				✓				Some gardens have been block-paved to create hardstanding for resident's cars. Lots of nice tubs
d Quality of upkeep, including gates, fences, paths		✓						Generally well maintained
Streets – routeway environment								
e Pavement quality – width, surface, excrement, obstacles, litter, street furniture						✓		Wide pavements but uneven surface, prolific dog fouling, some cars parked on pavement edge
f Road quality – congestion, noise, safety, parking						✓		Rather busy road, no traffic calming measures
g Landscaping – trees, greens, grass strips	✓							Double row of leafy, healthy mature trees
Amenities – service environment								
h Proximity and quality of community services – local shops, play areas, church	✓							Parade of shops on main street nearby, popular local school and park, strong sense of community
i Accessibility to public transport and parking			✓					Frequent local bus service, on-street parking

How would you feel about living in this area?   Fine ☐ OK ☐ Not sure ☐ Doubtful ☐ No way ☐

Notes to Figure 3
* Use split scores as appropriate (e.g. criteria 'e' is scored at -2/3, which equals -2 1/2)
* It helps if the group has an agreed standard of scoring on a bi-polar scale before the actual assessment takes place. The group must also agree a set of appropriate criteria for the survey, e.g. by discussing a range of streetscape photographs beforehand.
* This technique poses problems in some contexts, e.g. where there is a great variety of property within the same area, at varying standards of upkeep. How do you score criteria 'c' and 'd' in terraced streets without front gardens, for example?

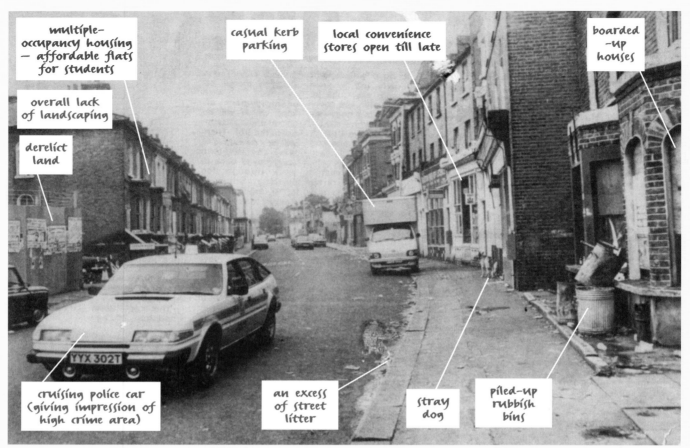

multiple-occupancy housing – affordable flats for students

casual kerb parking

local convenience stores open till late

boarded-up houses

overall lack of landscaping

derelict land

cruising police car (giving impression of high crime area)

an excess of street litter

stray dog

piled-up rubbish bins

Look closely at Figure 4. You may think this image is 'typical' of an inner-city area in the early 1980s – i.e. it reinforces a stereotype – but this is only one perception. If you experienced this environment as one of its residents you might feel very differently about it because of your culture and local knowledge (e.g. proximity to the city centre nightlife).

Figure 4: An inner-city street scene (photograph taken in the early 1980s). Labelling in red indicates a probable negative impression.

Beach quality surveys

UP TO ONE DAY

For the best results, when comparing two or more tourist beaches make the surveys during the high season and under good weather conditions. The same technique can be used to evaluate a range of popular leisure activities.

In Figure 5, there are several criteria for each of the five main categories (the Safety category is used as a worked example, see below). Each category is scored out of 20 points (totalling 100), though because of their importance, the Safety and Physical categories could well be weighted at 25/30 points each, particularly where children are concerned. You will have to work out your own breakdown of points for each criteria within a category. For example, for category A, Safety (30 points), this might be:

• beach slope = 5
• sea currents = 6
• lifeguard/first aid = 3
• breaking waves = 2
• inshore water quality = 3
• offshore wind = 4
• hazards (in water/on beach) = 3
• busy roads = 4

You can count and categorise the numbers and type of people using the beach, and do an activity survey (see pages 14-15). For example, user categories might be:

Children ☐   Teenagers/young adults ☐

Adults ☐   Pensioners ☐

You could map and account for the **distribution** of beach users, placing dots on a **large-scale** sketch map of the beach. Sunbathers, surfers, holidaying families, older people and walkers will all have different preferences and expectations concerning beaches as an amenity. (A useful source for details of the European Blue Flag Scheme and Seaside Award Beaches is the Tidy Britain Group on www.tidybritain.org.uk).

B Access	Car parking (capacity, cost, security, distance); availability of public transport, distance from resort, quality of approach roads and footpaths, road signs, disabled access, etc.	15
C Physical	Type of beach material, size and shape of beach, extent of litter, sea weed and flotsam, beach **aspect** and exposure (hours of direct sunlight, degree of shade and wind), typical weather conditions	25
D Amenities	Existence and quality of toilets, shops, deckchairs and recliners, water sports facilities, waste bins and public telephones, information boards, promenade, benches and shelter, etc.	20
E Aesthetic	The natural beauty of a beach within it's local environment, i.e. rocks, cliffs, sand dunes, streams, islands, natural vegetation, wildlife. The intrusiveness of built structures including coastal defences	10

Figure 5: Beach quality categories and point scores out of 100 for one beach.

Attitude surveys

Most commercial and public organisations are now conducting quality surveys to assess the acceptability of their services or products. In the field of human geography, many studies involve the gauging and recording of people's attitudes and feelings, particularly with respect to local issues such as car parking provision, traffic management, vandalism, council tax, etc. These surveys are usually done using interviews or questionnaires (Figure 6).

Q5. Overall, how would you rate the staff who teach your favourite AS-level subject(s)? (see Figure 6a.)

Q6. We want the student services in this college to be excellent. In which areas should we prioritise any improvements? Please tick the relevant boxes and include your comments in the last column. (see Figure 6b.)

a)

The staff are:	Strongly agree (1)	Agree (2)	Uncertain (3)	Disagree (4)	Strongly disagree (5)
Friendly and helpful	✓				
Well organised			✓		
Knowledgeable				✓	

Note: Despite the anonymity of these surveys, many respondents tend to 'play safe' by avoiding extreme responses. The five response categories are numbered to facilitate statistical processing.

b)
a) Improved social/recreational areas	- we tend to collect in odd bits of space
b) Help with further education applications	
c) More say in the disposal of college funds	- we should be spending more on student facilities
d) Better access to ICT and photocopying facilities -	saturated during busy periods of the week
e) Guidance/counselling services	
f) Wider choice of food in the refectory	

Figure 6: Extracts from a survey of college students.

Mental maps

Mental maps are often used to determine how people's knowledge of locational landmarks is influenced by such things as their age, gender, cultural background, length of residence, income level, degree of mobility, etc. Such maps can greatly enhance a study and have not been 'over-used' in the past. You will need multiple copies of pre-prepared base maps.

A typical study title might be: 'People of different age groups from the same residential area tend to have different perceptions of distances, boundaries, and the location of prominent features'. The method to follow might be as shown below:

1. Respondents are asked to name certain streets, prominent buildings, development sites, etc., the position of which has been marked on a base map (Figure 7).

2. Respondents are asked to give the distance from their home to a number of key sites, e.g. their workplace, a retail park, a football ground, a cinema.

3. Respondents are asked to mark on to a street map the 'perceived' boundary of their residential neighbourhood, given some fixed points as clues (e.g. local shops, a school, a church). Some of the fixed points may be well outside the neighbourhood zone. (Note: Children tend to have a very 'restricted' view of their surroundings, as do some people with mobility problems.)

4. Respondents are asked to draw their own map of their home town given just a few reference points (e.g. central railway station, main park). (Note that in some American cities surveys have found dramatic differences between ethnic groups in terms of the scale of the area they draw, and the amount of detail included on their maps.)

Figure 7: A sample base map with appropriate questions.

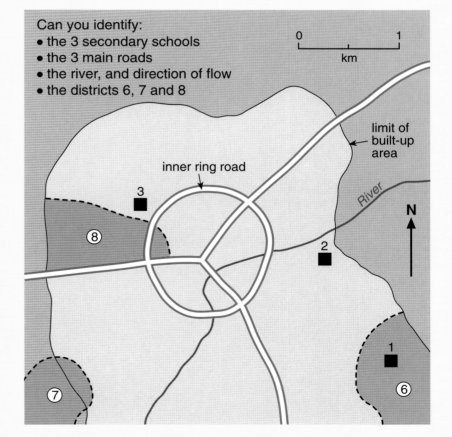

Can you identify:
- the 3 secondary schools
- the 3 main roads
- the river, and direction of flow
- the districts 6, 7 and 8

'Geography with attitude', *Geography Review*, vol. 8, no. 4, May 1995.

page 45

Key Skills

In an increasingly competitive job market, it is vital to be able to demonstrate that you have acquired a range of key skills. From September 2000, key skills – particularly 'communication' – will become an important part of GCSE and Advanced GCSE, and will be recognised by universities and employers. Although key skills can be developed in all subject areas, geography coursework provides a particular 'hot-spot' opportunity to develop the full range, or as the 'missing link' in your portfolio.

Photo: Catrin Treanor

Levels of skill

The new Key Skills will be 'signposted' in the awarding body specifications, and will be available at a number of levels. You should be able to access Level 3, which is consistent with Advanced GCSE. For some skills you may only be able to hit Level 2 (equivalent to higher tier GCSE), but in others, e.g. IT, it may be possible to score Level 4. The higher the Key Skills level, the more UCAS points you get.

How and when to use the core skills

Communication
This is about being able to discuss, listen, read, process and produce written material. Make sure the coursework is 'fit for purpose' and note the following:

- don't exceed your maximum word length;
- organise the report logically, with one section following on naturally from the preceding one, and with a clear development of your main points/ argument;
- show that you can reduce large volumes of information to the essentials;
- don't be too wordy – keep the text clear and simple but use specialist vocabulary as necessary;
- write legibly and make sure that your spelling, punctuation and grammar are accurate.

Application of number
Your numeracy skills will be shown by the way that you process raw data (e.g. size, scale, area, volumes, averages, range, formulae and equations, ratios, percentages and fractions). It is important to include a range of presentational techniques in your study (e.g. graphs, tables, scale drawings), as well as evidence of complex multi-stage calculations such as river discharge or proportional change. **Quantitative** studies (e.g. traffic surveys) which produce large data sets (over 50 items) are ideal contexts for using this key skill, but resist using complex calculations, in largely **qualitative** studies (e.g. EQAs).

Information technology
If you word-process your coursework then it will provide evidence of a range of IT skills (e.g. appropriate choice of type styles and layout, ability to use the spell check and word count tools correctly). The value of information and communications technology (ICT) is that it helps to save you time on basic processing activities, and enables you to acquire and make decisions about information from a range of sources (e.g. the Internet, large databases, CD-ROMs, scanned images, geographical information systems, spreadsheets, computer generated graphs and charts). Using ICT, you can also interact with other students via e-mail, and use intranet systems to download and collect or exchange data.

Information technology = 'IT'
Information and communications technology can be used to search, select, explore, develop and exchange information, thus developing your IT skills.

Communication = 'C'
This skill runs like a continuous thread through your coursework. Up to 15% of the total coursework mark is based on report organisation and quality of written work.

Problem solving = 'PS'
If your coursework is not issue-based, there is still the problem of completing your coursework to specification, and on time!

So what are these Key Skills?

Improving your own learning and performance = 'LP'
Coursework allows you to plan and monitor your activities and their progress.

Application of number = 'N'
This skill is about being able to gather information, to plan how to use it, to carry out calculations and to present findings.

Working with others = 'WO'
Most coursework is group-based and involves group decisions and teamwork.

Key

Core key skills: These are the central skills – they will collect premium points for UCAS applications.

Wider key skills: These skills are of particular interest to employers. Just because these skills cannot easily be assessed from written material, it doesn't mean that you are not judged on them.

'Developing Key Skills through geography fieldwork', *Teaching Geography*, vol. 24, no. 3, July 1999.

How and when to use the wider skills

Geography coursework – especially residential fieldwork – provides an ideal opportunity to demonstrate your wider skills. For example by:

• producing an action plan with a manageable time schedule;

• working as a constructive member of a group or team, with an agreed role, supporting others and learning from them;

• reviewing your own individual progress;

• evaluating the group's success and your own success or performance within it;

• identifying and overcoming difficulties, suggesting how the job could have been done better.

Many geography enquiries are issues-based; they focus on a problem and often suggest solutions. For example, a study of a controversial planning issue offers opportunities to develop problem-solving and other key skills. Remember, the actual execution and delivery of your coursework on time is a 'problem' in itself, particularly given pressures from other subjects you might be studying, from paid work, and/or from a hectic social life. So, if you can crack that one you are well on the way!

Redeveloping an under-used area of land (a sample study)

This group activity (10-12 students) could focus on a range of sites, e.g. derelict land or vandalised areas; land liable to flooding, contamination or subsidence; school/college/centre grounds; **greenfield/brownfield sites** earmarked for development.

Problem: *Can the land use, including buildings, be changed or enhanced in ways that better meet customer need?*

The example shown in Figure 1 is based on a weekend Key Skills course which focused on the estate and grounds attached to a residential field centre.

Figure 1: Sequence of activities and associated Key Skills for a group activity in the grounds of a field study centre.

These codes refer to the official Key Skills criteria. For example, PS3.1: 'PS' = Problem solving, '3' = Level 3, '1' refers to the first criteria (which requires that a problem exists with no immediate solution in this example). Each criteria will require two pieces of evidence.

Stage 1	**Groupwork:** Define the problem, including standards for a solution, and discuss the nature and scale of the problem. Who/what determines whether the solution is up to standard? Decide what information is needed.	PS3.1, C3.1a, N3.1
Stage 2	**Groupwork:** Decide on individual roles and resources, time scales and risk factors through an action plan. Appoint a group leader and observer(s). Identify factors which might be problematic and consider strategies to overcome these challenges.	PS3.2, WO3.1 LP3.1
Stage 3	**Individual activities:** Data collection phase – primary and secondary (within defined roles):	N3.2, C3.2 IT3.1

Primary data collection	Secondary data collection
Land-use map, including buildings (based on existing base-map) **EQAs** (individual and group) **Questionnaires** (current users, paid staff and workers and local community) **Risk Assessment Statement** **Identification of priority features** (e.g. 'cosy spots', entrances, main signs, mature trees, and 'problem spots' such as vandalised walls/benches) **Interviews** (with actual decision-makers) **Monitor user movements** (along footpaths, etc.)	Obtain existing **site management plan and policy statements** Research **capital constraints**, to keep exercise financially realistic (budgets) Research **past record of usage** if possible (e.g. age, gender, **socio-economic** background/**catchment**) Search the **Internet** for related examples and issues Contact the **local authority** to find out about any planning limitations or constraints that may be imposed

Stage 4	**Whole-group review** meetings, maybe twice a day, where each individual reports back on progress and identifies problem areas and/or where they need assistance.	WO3.2, LP3.2 N3.3
Stage 5	**Individual presentations** of findings to the rest of the group, e.g. use of a land-use map with scale, key and shading. Poster display identifying the range of user views. Tape recording of interview with local planner and the decision maker. Use a multimedia presentation, e.g. *PowerPoint*, to display information.	PS3.4, C3.1b
Stage 6	Formal group discussion of alternative management strategies, bearing in mind that two options are required, e.g. redesign/redevelop in terms of a low-cost or high-cost alternative, or short-term or longer-term, or environmental option v economic option, or client option v community option.	C3.3, IT3.3
Stage 7	Present the agreed management plan to the external standardiser or decision maker. Possibly use ICT for spatial display, e.g. digital maps and geographical information systems. Create a new promotional website. Reflect on how the group performed and how they might improve their actions in the future.	WO3.3, LP3.3

Provided that the main focus of the above example is clearly geographical or environmental, it has the potential to be converted into a useful piece of 2000-3000 word coursework. Individual reports can be written up (focusing on the role of the individual), set in the context of the group's discussions. Running notes of the main events actions from the weekend will be required as evidence.

The Qualifications and Curriculum Authority has produced a 'Student guide' for each Key Skill. These free four-page booklets will allow you to become familiar with the number/letter codings used for Key Skills. Ask your teacher for more information or visit the QCA website: qca.org.uk

Land Use Mapping

Any permanent or semi-permanent feature that takes up space on the ground, from a pillar box to a factory, qualifies for inclusion on a land use map. Geographers make much use of such maps, and often generate their own from detailed surveys. One such is the Geographical Association's 1996 'Land Use-UK'. There is no limit to the range of sizes and types of area that can be mapped: it may be an area as small as your school/college buildings and grounds or as large as a countryside park or city centre. Land use maps do not exist for large parts of the UK, so producing your own is a good opportunity to do some original work.

Base map reproduced from the Ordnance Survey material with the permission of The Controller of Her Majesty's Stationery Office, © Crown Copyright Licence number MC 100030715.

Land use mapping as part of coursework

The preparation of a land use map does not in itself qualify as a stand-alone coursework project; it must have an associated purpose. For example, a land use map would be an essential element in a study to do with conflicting land uses in an area (e.g. **segregation** of industrial and residential estates, cycle paths and roadways, landfill sites and areas of public open space). See Figure 3, which also shows the scope for annotation skills with this technique.

Land use maps are powerful tools for helping you to identify **temporal** changes in an area, such as changes in the use of fields at different times of year or from one year to another. For such a study you could make your own land use maps and, if published maps are available for earlier years, compare them to see how the land use has changed over time (clues include field sizes, farm buildings, woodland cover, lines of hedges/fences). Other useful mapped sources of information include geology maps at the 1:25 000 and 1:50 000 scale, land capability maps (see Appendix) and soil classification maps. These help to show how land use is influenced by physical **factors** such as bedrock, soils and slopes. As well as maps, some farmers have written, mental or visual records of changes to their land and property.

On the basis of what you discover, you could try making a prediction about what may happen to the patterns of land use in the future, for example, speculate where further pedestrianised zones may be created in town centres.

How to do it

1. Think carefully about your sampling strategy. If your area is relatively small, e.g. an out-of-town retail park or a small rural village, then you can probably map the whole site. If you are going to map a large area then you should consider using **transect** surveys along selective main routes, for example (Figure 1). You will need to work in a group.

2. Find a suitable **large-scale** map of your study area (the local library should have one). An Ordnance Survey map at a scale of 1:10 000, or larger, is ideal for most cases. Local Authorities may produce detailed street maps, and Goad plans are very useful for studies of central business districts.

3. Design your classification system. This involves dividing the major land use categories into a number of sub-divisions. Thus, the residential category could be split according to either age or style of building (many inner-city areas date from the Victorian period – 1830s to about 1900 – and houses are often terraced in style). There is a land use classification key in the Appendix – see page 104.

4. Build up your map in the field, using a system of letters and numbers (e.g. a toilet would carry the coding E8 – see urban land use key in Appendix). Back at base, you might re-draw the map and/or colour code the land uses with a key.

Land Use-UK 1996

In 1996 students from 1500 UK schools took part in a national survey of the land-use in the UK. Discover whether your school took part in the Survey, you may be able to compare and contrast copies of the Land Use-UK 1996 maps with the ones you produce.

ICT links

You can use a computer to scan in a land use map, then divide it into gridded squares. This may be easier and quicker than hand drawing.
Some websites provide maps (not land use) which can be downloaded, for example, http://www.mapquest.com and http://www.ordsvy.gov.uk. This could save you time hunting in the library.

Limitations

• Obtaining land use maps as secondary data (e.g. Goad maps or larger scale Ordnance Survey maps such as the 1:10 000 or 1:2500) could prove expensive if they are not available at school/college or in the local studies library (where you may only be allowed to photocopy a single A4 extract from the whole sheet).

• Mapping large areas is time consuming and laborious (so this is a good opportunity for group work).

Transect surveys (for large urban areas)

- Select a routeway that radiates from the town centre to the suburbs (Figure 1).

- Tally each **function** that fronts the road on each side, ground level only, as in Figure 2.

- You may be able to establish a **relationship** between functional dominance and distance away from the CBD, e.g. in the first 200m retail use should dominate (**modal** category).

Note: Belt transects may be more appropriate in some locations – (see 'Sampling Techniques' page 78).

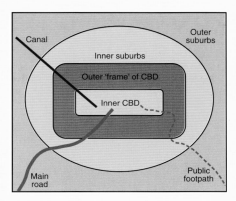

Figure 1: Selecting a routeway.

Equipment

- Base maps
- Note book, clipboard, coloured pens/pencils
- Land use classification key (see Appendix)

Figure 2 has only five basic land use categories – for your own surveys, you will need to sub-divide these to create a more 'finely-tuned' picture of land use. In this example, for each side of the road one tally was made every 25m, giving eight tallies for every 200m. The tallies are put under the L (left) or R (right) column according to which side of the road was being recorded (the left side in this case is the left-hand side as you walk out of the CBD).

Figure 2: An extract from tally chart compiled along 2km of the A49 in Ludlow.

Name(s) .... Direction of transect ....

Date .... Start .... Finish ....

Distance (m)	Residential		Retail		Commercial/ professional		Industrial		Recreational	
	L	R	L	R	L	R	L	R	L	R
0-200		/	ЖЖ	ЖЖ	///	//				
201-400	//	//	///	////	//	//	/			
401-600	///	////	///	//		/		/	//	

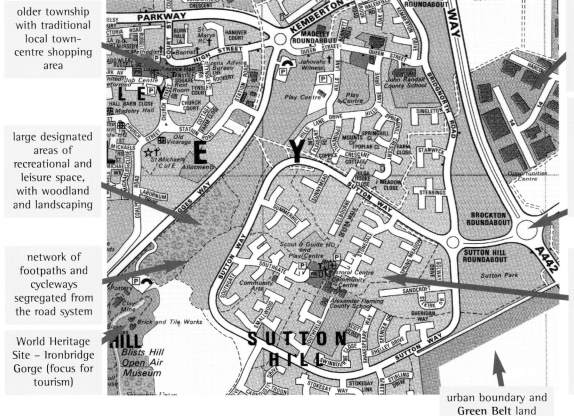

older township with traditional local town-centre shopping area

large designated areas of recreational and leisure space, with woodland and landscaping

network of footpaths and cycleways segregated from the road system

World Heritage Site – Ironbridge Gorge (focus for tourism)

modern industrial zone segregated from the residential areas by a dual carriageway

planned road system with large roundabouts providing good accessibility via service or feeder roads

evidence of 'neighbourhood estate' planning, e.g. integral community facilities, perimeter roads, safe cul-de-sacs without through roads

urban boundary and **Green Belt** land

Figure 3: Extract from land use map of Telford New Town, 1986. Source: Telford District Council.

'Land of many uses', *Geography Review*, vol. 6, no. 2, November 1992.

page **49**

Microclimate Investigations

Climate is the average weather conditions of a place or region throughout the seasons – it influences what crops can be grown, what we wear, our leisure activities and even our moods. Weather is the physical state of the atmosphere at a particular time. At the global scale, climate is governed by such things as latitude and proximity to oceans but local climates vary depending on such things as **topography** and altitude. At a much smaller scale, climate may be modified by individual land uses such as high buildings or belts of trees, and it is in this context that the term 'microclimate' is used.

Photo: Diane Wright

As well as being determined by land uses, microclimate can in turn have a dramatic effect on how land is used. This is why urban planners, farmers and others need to understand the causes and effects of microclimate, and to be able to measure the various elements and variations. As the subject for a fieldwork exercise, microclimate is an ideal topic: investigations can be made close to home and in a variety of settings ranging from your front garden to the school/college grounds, a woodland, a lake, a hillside or part of an urban area. Also, the sampling procedure is usually straightforward and logical and provides **quantitative** results.

Aspects of microclimate that can be measured

6 Cloud cover and type, visibility and sunshine hours: (see Other ideas on page 53)

5 Air pressure: this might change at different altitudes and under different weather conditions, i.e. as a 'front' passes overhead.

4 Relative humidity: this varies according to air temperature, but is also influenced by water features such as a lake or pond.

3 Wind: speed and direction will vary according to exposure, shelter and altitude, as well as influences from the built environment. (Note: Coastal locations tend to be windier than inland ones.)

1 Rainfall: variations due to exposure and shelter, e.g. comparisons between different woodland types and the effect of interception.

2 Temperature: measurements of air, ground surfaces, soil and water. (Note that temperature is influenced by wind speed – wind-chill effects).

Project ideas

Figures 1 and 2 provide two examples of environments where you could carry out a microclimate survey using some of the equipment described on pages 52-53. Other ideas for projects are as follows:

1. Planning an urban garden (e.g. a roof garden), with reference to, for example, **aspect**, wind, shelter, rainwater collection, temperature extremes relating to hard surfaces. Think about what might grow/not grow in different parts of the garden, and where is best for seating at different seasons, etc.

2. Investigating the microclimate of a hillside, where aspect, altitude and exposure will all have an effect.

3. Investigating the microclimate of a wood. The key **variables** are type of tree (coniferous and deciduous), planting density, age of **stand** and season (most noticeable are changes in temperature, wind speed and humidity through the seasons). It is interesting to note differences in the microclimate inside and immediately outside a woodland.

Steps to take

1. Before finally deciding on a project, check what equipment is available to you, how much time you have (some microclimate studies involve taking measurements at intervals over a long period and/or at particular seasons), what secondary data is needed, what locations are realistic in terms of accessibility, etc.

2. Decide on an experimental aim and develop some initial **hypotheses**, for example, air temperatures will peak at 14.00hrs during the day.

3. Obtain a **large-scale** map or town plan of your chosen area/sites (e.g. 1:25 000 or 1:10 000). For small sites, consider making your own sketch map.

4. Decide on your sampling strategy, including the number of sites you will be using and what measurements will be taken at each site.

5. Identify dates when you will be available to take your measurements. Look at the weather forecast and then fix a specific time or date. Remember that for many studies you will want to make comparisons so the microclimate readings will need to be synchronised (this has implications regarding personnel and use of shared equipment).

Limitations

- Basic daily data (see below) is available free from some of the 500 local meteorological stations in Britain. A charge of about £25 is made for computer extraction of non-standard data. Check the Met Office website (http://www.met-office.gov.uk) for more information.

- Most of the equipment you will use will lack the sensitivity needed to record minor, but significant, microclimate changes.

- Your school/college may not have the specialist equipment.

Sample studies

A small-scale study

Figure 1 shows some features you might find in the local area (i.e. an area of small scale). It gives you some ideas for sites (see numbers 1-6) where microclimate measurements might be made.

1. This site, close to a body of water, may influence the local temperature and humidity.

2. Trees act as an interception layer and are buffer zones against the wind.

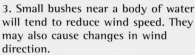

3. Small bushes near a body of water will tend to reduce wind speed. They may also cause changes in wind direction.

4. Tarmac surfaces will show temperature extremes.

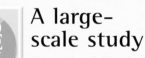

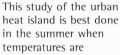

5. Buildings act as a windbreak and also modify temperatures, e.g. radiate heat during the summer. You may be able to measure the effect of aspect on temperature at different times of the day.

6. Buildings close together may create wind-tunnel effects. This is called the Venturi Effect.

Figure 1: Where to locate microclimates. Photos: Paula Richardson

Equipment

- Thermometers, rain gauges
- Anemometer/ventimeter, compass
- Beaufort Scale (Figure 7)
- Barometer, whirling psychrometer
- Large-scale maps of area
- Recording sheets

UP TO HALF A DAY (FOR ONE SET OF MEASUREMENTS)

Some points to note

- Spread out your sites and, using stratified sampling (see page 77), pick places where you expect to find differences in the microclimate. You should use a range of sites (in Figure 1 there are six).

- Recording times will vary. If you are looking at, for example, changes in precipitation between different areas, you will need to record the precipitation collected every day. If you are investigating **diurnal** fluctuations in temperature and humidity, you need to take measurements on a regular basis, perhaps every 2-4 hours.

A large-scale study

UP TO ONE DAY

This study of the urban heat island is best done in the summer when temperatures are highest. The aim is to demonstrate that artificial surfaces such as tarmac, concrete and brick, heat up more rapidly and retain heat longer than natural surfaces such as soil or grass.

Measurements (standardised to shade or sun) need to be taken at the same time at different locations, so this is best suited to group work. The **transect** line must pass through markedly different urban or urban-fringe environments (Figure 2). One-off sampling is not advised. Ideally, measurements should be at hourly intervals (e.g. from 8.00am to night-time).

In some cities, the urban heat island may be such that it encourages convectional atmospheric activity leading to localised thunder/lightning or heavy rainfalls. These in turn can cause flash flooding and other problems.

Figure 2: Investigating the urban heat island.

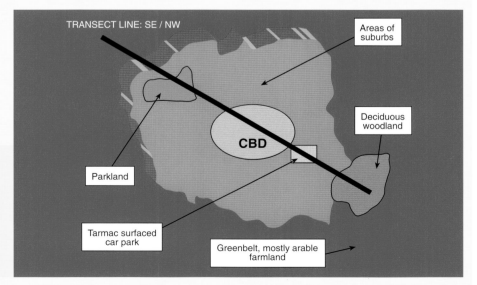

'Urban heat islands', *Geography Review*, vol. 11, no. 3, January 1998.

Measuring equipment

1. Rainfall (in millimetres)

Rainfall is measured using a rain gauge. Gauges are not expensive to buy, but you can make one yourself using a funnel and jar or tin (Figure 3). If you need more than one funnel for your project, make sure they are all of the same diameter so that it is a fair test (the British standard gauge is 5 inches.

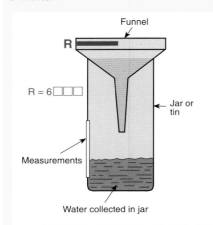

Figure 3: Rain gauge.

Site your rain gauges carefully – they should be clear of buildings and trees (shelter and interception will affect the results). Also note that gauges which are raised above the ground tend to under-estimate the rainfall because of eddies which take the rain past the collection funnel, and gauges which are sited flush with the ground surface may be affected by rain splash. Leave out for 24 hours and transfer the water collected (if any) to a measuring cylinder. Calculate the amount of precipitation in millimetres:

$$\frac{1000 \times \text{volume of rain in ml}}{3.14 \times R \times R} = \text{rainfall (mm) in 24 hours}$$

Where R is the radius of the funnel in millimetres (Figure 3).

Worked example:

$$\frac{1000 \times 12}{3.14 \times 60 \times 60} = \frac{12\,000}{11\,304} = 1.06\text{mm in 24hr}$$

Note: Average annual UK rainfall is about 750mm.

2. Temperature (in °C)

Two main types of thermometer are available:

a) Digital thermometers: these give **precise** readings to 0.1°C, but can be unreliable if incorrectly **calibrated** or if the batteries run low (check before use).

b) Analogue thermometers (mercury or alcohol): these are made of glass so there is risk of breakage, but they are reliable and should be **accurate** to at least 0.5°C. Beware of false readings due to hand contact with the bulb.

The best place to take temperature measurements is in the shade, unless you are investigating aspect, in which case measurements in and out of the sun are needed.

Air: take measurements at a set height, say 1m above ground, so all temperatures will be comparable.

Ground: support a thermometer horizontally on small blocks 1-2cm above the ground, or rest the temperature probe at this height (don't let the probe come into direct contact with the ground surface). Ground temperatures are more extreme than air temperatures – either hotter or colder.

Soil: dig a small hole in the soil, 20, 30 or 50cm deep. Lower the thermometer into the hole, loosely infill and leave for at least three minutes. Remove and read the temperature (soil probes can be pushed straight into the soil). Soil temperatures show low diurnal fluctuations, especially at greater depths.

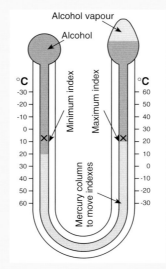

Figure 4: Maximum/minimum thermometer.

The daily temperature range is the difference between the hottest and coldest air temperatures each day, and it is measured using a maximum and minimum thermometer which has small markers (indexes) that show maximum and minimum extremes (Figure 4). Temperature range data may be more valuable than a one-off temperature reading.

3. Wind speed and direction (in kph or m/s and compass degrees)

Wind speed can be recorded and measured in different ways:

a) Anemometer (Figure 5): a high quality instrument which will work in near still conditions. It is effective and reliable, but expensive (£100-£200 – so don't assume your school/college will have one).

b) Ventimeter (Figure 6): fairly cheap (approximately £20) and reasonably accurate but doesn't work in low wind conditions.

c) Beaufort Scale (Figure 7): the basis for making a **qualitative** assessment of wind speed based on evidence around you (e.g. smoke rising vertically = 0).

Figure 5: An anemometer.

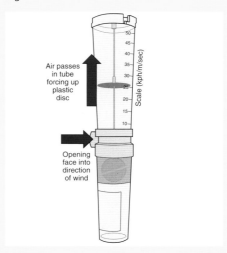

Figure 6: A ventimeter.

Force	Description	Mean wind speed (kph)
0	Calm – smoke rises vertically	0
1	Light air – smoke drifts in the wind	5
2	Light breeze – wind felt on face	10
3	Gentle breeze – leaves and small twigs move	15
4	Moderate breeze – loose paper moves	25
5	Fresh breeze – small trees sway	35
6	Strong breeze – large branches sway, umbrellas difficult to use	45
7	Near gale – difficult to walk in this, whole trees sway	55
8	Gale – small twigs break off, extreme walking difficulty	70
9	Strong gale – possibility of structural damage	80
10	Storm – trees uprooted, structural damage	90
11	Violent storm – rare, widespread damage	110
12	Hurricane – you had better run away if you see this one coming	120

Figure 7: The Beaufort Scale.

Originally based on the effect that wind speed had on a fully-rigged sailing ship, Admiral Beaufort devised this scale to help determine the amount of sail the ship should put up or use in different levels of wind. The scale has since been adapted for use on land.

To calculate wind direction you need a compass and something that can be blown easily by the wind (e.g. grass cuttings or leaves thrown up in the air, a small flag on a stick, or a home-made wind sock). Alternatively, you could make your own wind vane (Figure 8).

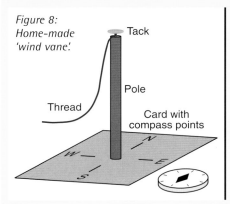

Figure 8: Home-made 'wind vane'.

Tack
Pole
Thread
Card with compass points

4. Relative humidity (in percentage)

All air contains water vapour. Only when it is misty, foggy or very cold can this vapour be seen. In high humidity conditions, evaporation rates are reduced and the air feels muggy or 'close' (as in a tropical rainforest). In lower humidity environments, like deserts, the rate of evaporation is higher and the air feels 'fresher'.

The best way to measure **relative humidity** is by using a whirling psychrometer (Figure 9). Whirl the device above your head for a minute and take

Figure 9: Using a whirling psychrometer.

readings from the 'wet' and 'dry' bulb thermometers. Relative humidity is based on the differential between these two (see Appendix for conversion table). When the wet and dry bulb temperatures are equal it means the air is saturated and can hold no more water vapour. An alternative measuring instrument is a wet-and-dry bulb hygrometer but it is less portable and is usually found fixed within a **Stevenson Screen**.

5. Air pressure (in millibars)

Air pressure is measured by a barometer. High pressures can reach as much as 1040 mb, while low pressures can go down to 960 mb. Aneroid barometers (Figure 10) are quite accurate, relatively portable and usually easy to find (as well as asking at school/college, ask family friends – they may have one hanging on the wall at home).

Figure 10: A barometer.

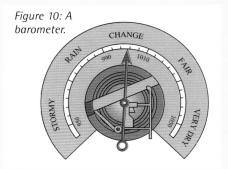

Hints and tips

- Don't expect to find significant variations in, for example, temperature, rainfall or humidity at different points within a small area unless there are major differences in surface cover (e.g. concrete v soil).

- Readings from instruments must be as **accurate** as possible because microclimatic changes are often subtle and slight. For example, temperature may only change by a matter of a few tenths of a degree between two sites or at different times of the day.

- Provide a brief site description at each location where measurements are taken. Features such as overhanging trees or tall buildings may affect wind speed, sunshine, temperature, etc., so you need to describe these and estimate their height. Photographs are also useful as evidence.

Other ideas

Cloud cover: this has an affect on temperature and humidity so is something worth measuring. The amount of cloud cover is measured in oktas (eighths of the sky), e.g. overcast sky = 8 oktas. Cloud type is also worth recording (e.g. cirrus, cumulus).

Sunshine: the standard measuring equipment used by tourist resorts, etc., a Campbell-Stokes recorder, is usually expensive, but your school/college may have one. Alternatively, use a light meter to measure intensity.

Visibility: this can be measured using known landmarks in your local area and an Ordnance Survey map to calculate actual distances. On a clear day (and depending on altitude) you might be able to see at least 30km.

'Studies in microclimatology', *Teaching Geography*, vol. 22, no. 4, October 1997.

page 53

Note Taking and Recording

Traditionally, fieldwork has been conducted as if it were an extension of the classroom into the field. Typically, it involved groups of students listening to their teacher and trying to take notes in often difficult and distracting circumstances; the colder, wetter and windier it became, the quicker the classic symptoms of **fieldwork fatigue** set in. Times have changed, however, and the responsibility has been passed to you, the student. One of the consequences is that you will need to think far more carefully about the skill of recording what you are doing, what you are thinking, and even what sensations you are feeling.

How and when to use

Fieldwork is all about collecting and recording information, but it is not only in the field that you need to use note-taking skills; you may also need to take notes from textbooks, newspapers, lessons, and videos – often at speed. The trick is to focus on the key points being made, as well as key facts and figures. Use abbreviations, bullet points, short phrases and shorthand to save time, e.g. **pop.** (population), **ppt** (precipitation), **fw** (fieldwork), = (equals), >/< (increase/decrease).

It is a good idea to go back over your rough notes soon after taking them and, if necessary, to 're-work' them (a highlighter pen is useful at this point). You may decide to transform the notes into tabulations, **'talking heads'**, listed/numbered bullet points, spider diagrams (see 'Hints and tips' for an example) or even mental maps.

Hints and tips

5 Make sure that data recording sheets are prepared *before* going in to the field (Figure 1). All loose sheets of paper should be firmly bound, stapled or clamped together in the field otherwise they may be dropped or blown away by the wind.

6 Consider the use of personal tape recorders, dictaphones or memotakers for interviews, or for tutorials with your teacher, but make sure you have permission to use them beforehand. You can select the parts you want, and transcribe them later.

1 Don't forget the 'tools of the trade' – watch, pencils (that work well on damp paper), sharpener, rubber, pen, calculator, compass, etc. These are all small and easy to carry.

2 Note the location/day/time of each visit and, if appropriate, the weather conditions.

4 Use an A4 clipboard, particularly where data recording and field sketching is required. Attach a pencil on string to the clip, and use a transparent plastic wallet/bag to keep it dry, leaving enough room to enable you to work inside it (this is more difficult than it seems!). Rainproof clipboards can be purchased through athletics clubs.

3 A spiral bound A5-size notebook is best for most situations (it fits easily into a pocket). Stiffen the back with cardboard or sheet metal. Put your name, address and telephone number (home and school/college) inside the front cover.

Important points to remember

- Recording in the field is worth taking time over. Details are rapidly forgotten – rough scrawls, shorthand and 'floating' figures in a notebook may mean very little to you when you re-visit them a few days later. Also, remember that weeks or even months may pass between doing the fieldwork and producing the final report. This can be a real problem – the two operations become detached and the finished product suffers.

- Your field notebook and recording sheets are vital pieces of evidence so, regardless of their condition, they should be kept. You may need them when discussing the progress of your project with your teacher, and/or at an interview with the Examiner if your project is externally marked. Always include some proof of field recording in the primary data collection section of your report, or in the Appendix (this will depend on the official coursework guidelines).

ICT links

It is sound practice to save all word-processed material on a regular basis, and to keep a complete back-up copy on floppy disk or similar. As well as being an insurance against loss, this ensures that you have a copy of your work to refer to at a future date, perhaps for an interview relating to the project.

Recording sheets

A well prepared and pre-planned approach makes fieldwork recording and calculations much easier to do, and the results will be more accurate. This is why you need to design your recording sheets with great care, and to discuss them with other members of the group (if any) and your teacher before using them in the field. Above all, you must be clear about what information you want to obtain and how this connects to the purpose of your study. If appropriate, take along recording resources such as a dictaphone, species identification chart, pebble roundness chart, etc.

Figure 1 is an example of a recording sheet linked to a coursework investigation of the **relationship** between tree height, girth, light availability and spacing for certain species.

Notes

- It is usually quicker and easier to draw recording tables using a pen and ruler rather than a computer – spreadsheets can take time to 'customise' to suit varying widths of column headings, etc.
- Wherever possible, state the units of measurement in the column headings (e.g. luxes of light).
- It is good practice to include a 'comments' heading either at the end of each row (as in Figure 1) or as a panel at the foot of the recording sheet.
- It may be useful to include sufficient column space for a postage-stamp size of sketch (e.g. of leaves).

Equipment
- Notebook/clipboard
- 'Tools of the trade'
- Dictaphone/tape recorder

HOW LONG IS A PIECE OF STRING?

- By including the project title at the top of the recording sheet you are reminding yourself of the purpose of the fieldwork.

- In some cases, you may wish to record a range of values and to have a separate column to record the **mean** value. In Figure 1, the availability of incoming light may well vary according to the amount of canopy cover and the **aspect**, so readings for the four main compass directions have been included, together with their average.

DATA SHEET

PROJECT TITLE: .... NAME: ....

LOCATION: .... DAY/DATE/TIME: .... WEATHER: ....

TREE NO	TREE SPECIES	LEAF SKETCH	HEIGHT (M)	GIRTH AT CHEST LEVEL (M)	NEAREST NEIGHBOUR (M)	AVAILABLE LIGHT – N/S/E/W (LUXES)	MEAN	COMMENTS
1	common oak		27	2.65	11·7	750/1100 800/900	888	old tree, covered in ivy, some dead branches, a bit smelly.
2	silver birch		8	0·70	2·8	900/1300 850/1100	1040	mature tree in a grove of birches, evidence of bark disease

Figure 1: A field recording sheet.

Figure 2: Note taking in action? What are these students up to? Are they:
1. *inspired by the view?*
2. *observing and recording the inshore sediment transport system?*
3. *discretely going to the toilet?*
4. *taking a lunch break and reviewing their notes to date?*

OS Map Skills

Maps are plans or bird's eye views of the world, or a part of its surface. They are important geographical information systems in themselves, conveying a rich stream of secondary data. Nearly all coursework projects will make use of maps, particularly Ordnance Survey (OS) maps (so called because they were originally produced for military purposes – ordnance = mounted weapons). OS maps may be used in their own right, or for reference when producing introductory base maps on which the study area is **delimited** and described. A major bonus for you is that they are widely available in schools, colleges, libraries, bookshops and other outlets.

7 They are valuable tools for historical studies. For example, place names provide clues to the original site (e.g. 'acton' = clearing in an oak woodland) and hachures and different lettering styles tell us about past settlements. Also, if viewed in a series, maps can reveal significant changes over time (e.g. the 'lost' villages in the North Sea off the Holderness coast, East Yorkshire).

1 They allow sampling decisions to be made (e.g. in relation to river systems, **micro**climate studies, vegetation and soil surveys, urban **transects**, farm studies and transport surveys).

6 They highlight 'wildscapes' and their inaccessibility (e.g. very few buildings or settlements, unproductive land, few roads, semi-natural vegetation).

The Value of OS Maps

2 For urban areas, they enable different zones to be identified by showing such features as building density, street patterns, key **functions** and transport routeways.

5 By showing features such as field size, farm **distribution** and spacing, topography and slopes, and the extent of rough grazing, they suggest the intensity of agricultural land usage (though they don't reveal crop type, except woodland and orchards).

4 By showing features such as motorways, quarries, golf courses and National Parks, they reveal information relating to the commercial, industrial and amenity value of the countryside (as well as pressures upon the Green Belt).

3 Contours on maps show the height of the land above **mean** sea level (Ordnance Datum or OD) and so provide vital information regarding **topography**, particularly slopes.

Limitations

- Maps are merely 'snapshots' of frozen moments in time – they may be out-of-date even before they are published.

- Maps are expensive to buy and are not disposable items. They can easily be ruined by wind and rain, so make sure you protect them in a see-through plastic wallet, or use the laminated versions ('lamfold').

Note: Not all the features mentioned above appear on all maps – it depends on the scale. Thus, for example, field boundaries are not shown on 1:50 000 but are shown at larger scales 1:25 000 scale maps. This is why it is vital that you become familiar with OS maps at different scales, so that you can select the ones best suited to your chosen study (see Figure 2).

Hints and tips

- You must acknowledge the source of any maps that you copy: include the map scale, number and survey year, if relevant. Crown copyright applies to OS maps so unless your school has a composite licence, you can only photocopy an A4-sized colour extract from any OS sheet and any size in b/w (maps which are over 50 years old are copyright free). If your school does have a licence, then you can copy more material but you must remember to quote the licence number. Check with your teacher before you copy anything.

- Never include a full OS map in your report – it is a waste of money and space

and will be ignored by the Examiner. Photocopies are acceptable in your coursework (as are scanned or laser colour versions), but only if they carry extensive evidence that you have improved them through **annotation** and map work, and targeted them towards your particular enquiry.

- In many contexts, it helps to include a small inset map to give a wider **spatial** context to your study (see Figure 1).

- OS maps are not the only kind you can use; look for other local **large-scale** maps and plans such as street plans and tourist maps. For historical maps, check your local library and the County Records Office.

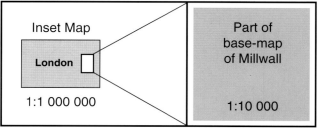

Figure 1: **Relationship** *of maps of different scales.*

The Service Level Agreement with local authorities allows all LA-funded schools to access digital map data free of charge. Check the Ordnance Survey website www.ordnancesurvey.gov.uk for details.

Scales

Ordnance Survey produces a wide variety of maps at different scales. Note that the grid lines are always 1km apart on 1:10 000, 1:25 000 and 1:50 000 (in real terms), and the area of each grid square is 1 sq km. There are 100 000cm in a kilometre, so dividing this figure by the scale number shown on the map will tell you how many centimetres on the map represent one kilometre on the ground (Figure 2).

Map scale and name	Grid size (1km)	Linear scale	Area covered (sq km)	Fieldwork usage
Superplan™ 1:1250	80 x 80cm	25m	0.25	Detailed site plans for housing, retail and industrial units – even garden sheds show up. This is the scale for **micro**-studies in urban areas.
Superplan™ 1:2500	40 x 40cm	50m	1	More detailed than street maps – individual houses, shops, works premises and pavements are shown.
Landplan® 1:10 000	10 x 10cm	200m	25	Shows broad patterns of land usage, both town and country – a suitable scale for farm studies and many urban studies.
Pathfinder®/ Explorer™ 1:25 000	4 x 4cm	500m	200 to 1000	More detailed maps, suitable for walkers – this scale allows sampling decisions to be made about rivers, vegetation, slopes, microclimate, etc.
Landranger® 1:50 000	2 x 2cm	1000m =1 km	1600	Road/cycle/walking maps covering large areas allowing broad interpretations to be made, e.g. rural settlement patterns.

Increasingly large scale →

The Superplan™ maps have been digitally customised since 1992 so you can now order your own tailor-made version (at a price).

Reminders and tips

- You can see from Figure 2 that the bigger the scale number (first column), the more shrinkage has taken place – larger areas can be covered but in increasingly less detail. Thus, at a scale of 1:200 million, the whole world can be reduced to a single A4 page. This is called a **small-scale** map, whereas one which shows a small area but in great detail is called a large-scale map.

- Reducing or enlarging a map scale in order to produce a sketch map is a skill that needs some time and practice to develop. The trick is to select a linear feature from the map – such as a straight section of road or a direct line distance between two obvious points – then to measure this length and convert it to the real distance using the map scale. As long as these indicator features appear on your sketch map, then you now know the real distance between them.

In Figure 3 two churches are shown which are known to be 4km apart. By measuring the distance between them you can derive the scale of your sketch map (if this distance is 8cm than the scale is 1:50 000).

Figure 2: Summary table of map scales and usage.

Map distance = 8cms

Real distance apart = 4km

So 8cms represents 4km (2cm = 1km) = 1:50,000

Figure 3: Deriving the scale of your map from known distances.

Areas

Reminders and tips

- Knowing that each grid square represents one 1 sq km, you can estimate the area of features such as towns, woodlands, river catchments, conservation sites, etc. First count up the whole squares occupied by the relevant land use, then 'patch' all the part squares together and estimate the overall total. Double-check this result or ask a colleague to do it (Figure 4).

- On large-scale maps (1:2500 and 1:1250) the kilometre grid squares are sub-divided into 100 **hectare** squares, each measuring 100m x 100m. A hectare is very similar to a full-size football pitch in area.

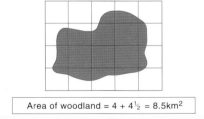

Area of woodland = $4 + 4\frac{1}{2} = 8.5km^2$

Figure 4: Calculating the area using grid squares.

Grid references

Reminders and tips

- When giving a grid reference, first read off from the vertical grid lines (called eastings) then from the horizontal lines (northings), starting in the bottom left (south-west) corner of the grid square that you are interested in. Thus, the four-figure grid reference for the lighthouse in Figure 5 is 78 62.

- To give a six-figure grid reference you divide each side of a square into 10 imaginary 'ant-steps' (Figure 5). Count the ant-steps out of 10 across the square, recording these steps as the third digit of the six-figure reference. Do the same up the square and record the steps as the sixth digit in the grid reference (e.g. the lighthouse is at GR 788 623).

- If a feature lies at the junction of an easting and a northing, the last digit in a six-figure grid reference will be zero for each grid line. Thus, the boulder in Figure 5 is at 790 629.

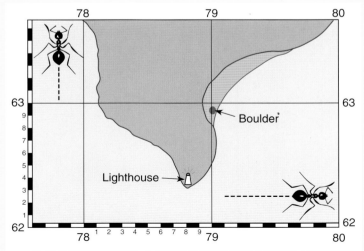

Figure 5: Working out grid references.

Hare, R.T. (1985) *A First Course in Mapwork.* Macmillan Education.

Directions

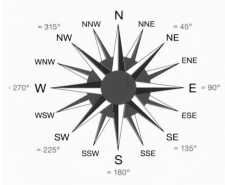

Figure 6: A compass rose (360°)

Reminders and tips

Knowing about directions is crucial for most studies you are likely to undertake – hence the reminder in Figure 6 (the four main directions shown are called cardinals, and the four intermediate directions, NE, SE, NW, SW, are called inter-cardinals). Remember also that as you look at a map east is to your right and west to your left (north is at the top).

Examples

- Building up a pattern of wind direction and speed over a few weeks (always remember to quote the compass bearing that the winds blow from, not towards).

- Orientation studies of glacial features such as corries and drumlins.

- Studying the influence of **aspect** on plant species, growth and distribution (e.g. some trees may show differences in branching, tree rings and moss growth).

- Studies of varying land-use and settlement patterns in relation to aspect (e.g. low-cost Victorian housing downwind of 'smoke-stack' factories in older industrial towns).

Q: You have built a house whose four walls all face south. A bear wanders by – what colour is it?

Gradients

Reminders and tips

- Contour lines provide strong clues as to the nature of slopes on a map: where they are tightly packed, height changes rapidly and so slopes are fairly steep; where they merge the ground will be very steep (e.g. crags, cliffs).

- Don't presume that the land is level in areas without contour lines – it could rise and fall within the limits of the contour interval (i.e. 10m at 1:50 000 and 5m at 1:25 000).

- Every fifth contour line is thickened to aid interpretation and each line will carry a numerical height somewhere along its sweep.

- To calculate gradient (defined as the average slope between two points), measure and work out:

$$\frac{\text{the vertical difference in metres between the two points}}{\text{the direct line or horizontal distance in metres between the two points}}$$

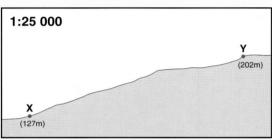

Figure 7

Q: Using Figure 7, calculate the gradient between points X and Y then convert it to a percentage by multiplying by 100, e.g. a gradient of 1:12 = 8.5%.

Cross-sections

Reminders and tips

- Cross-sections are vertical slices through the land surface, revealing variations in height and slope when viewed from the side. **Long profiles** of rivers and soil **catenas** are examples of cross-sections.

- Transect lines on a map can be converted to cross-sections using contour lines, as in Figure 8. Using a piece of paper which is at least as long as the transect line (A-B), place one edge along the line of transect and mark off each contour intersection with a pencil, including the height. Then draw the cross-section. As in Figure 8, using a suitable vertical scale (don't stretch this too much otherwise you will create an Alpine landscape). Include the trend of the transect line (e.g. NNW to SSE).

- Link the cross-section to your investigation by marking on such things as sampling points, land uses, significant features, vegetation zones, rock types, etc. Comment on the relationship between any of these features and the height and slope variations shown in the cross-section.

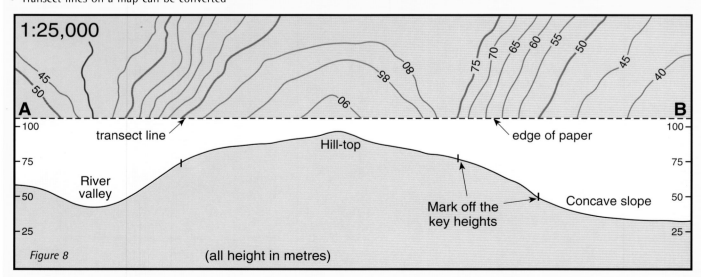

Figure 8 (all height in metres)

Using OS maps as aids to specific studies

River basins

OS maps are vital to the analysis of drainage basins. You can use them to identify and draw on the watershed which should delimit or separate your study **catchment area** from the adjacent ones. Within this you can estimate the catchment area and drainage density (the latter is calculated by dividing the catchment area in square kilometres by the total length in kilometres of all the stream channels within it). Finally, you can use the map to calculate the gradient, construct the long profile, mark on the direction of flows, and 'stream order' the channel system.

Spatial patterns

OS maps give a clear picture of settlement spacing, distribution and size **hierarchies** and can be related to models such as Christaller. They can also be used for nearest neighbour analysis and studies of spheres of influence.

Analysing changes over time

An historical sequence of maps can give a fascinating insight into change over time, particularly changes in the built and farmed environments. The example given in Figure 9 shows the same area (near Shrewsbury) at two dates 90 years apart, and illustrates a number of interesting changes during that period of time, as follows:

- Most significant is the change in land use from farmed land (at least 90% in 1888) to built-up, largely residential, land (nearly 70% in 1978).

- The Severn Valley railway line, long since disused, has been converted into a cycle track and footpath.

- Whereas in 1888 there were no 'amenity' land-uses (except for public footpaths), by 1978 a cricket ground, football fields and playing fields had all been established.

- Over the 90 years 'estate' property, such as Sutton Buildings have disappeared and been replaced by the Sutton Farm Estate and 'discrete' developments, such as a school with its own grounds, have been built.

- The Sutton Mill with its leat system (an artificial ditch to divert river water to provide power) has been demolished.

- Far more land is now occupied by roads and streets (about 10% by 1978) and the minor road shown at the bottom of these extracts has been widened and extended to form an inner bypass for Shrewsbury.

- Certain land uses have remained unchanged, e.g. the three shallow pools or meres (glacial kettle holes), and the flood-prone corridor of the Rea Brook (north-west corner).

Taken overall, these changes are typical of their time for areas close to large towns or cities, the main features being sub-urbanisation and pressure on the urban fringe for land-uses other than agriculture (e.g. for recreation).

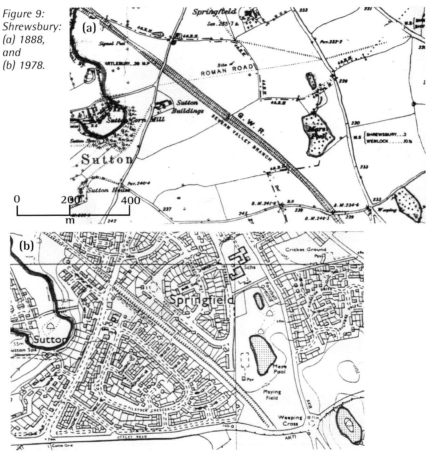

Figure 9: Shrewsbury: (a) 1888, and (b) 1978.

Mapping reproduced from the 1:25 000 scale Ordnance Survey sheet SJ41/51 (1978) with the permission of Her Majesty's Stationery Office © Crown copyright Licence number MC100030715.

And finally ...

- OS maps are not really land use maps: the extensive areas of 'white space' are unclassified. In the countryside these will be predominantly agricultural (e.g. rough grazing in upland areas).

- OS and all other maps are selective in what they show, and may distort certain features to give them particular prominence (e.g. on maps of most scales roads are shown at a width which is out of all proportion to reality). This is why you need to produce your own 'customised' sketch maps which, apart from their intrinsic value, also enable you to demonstrate particular skills such as use of scale and design ability. Such sketch maps are usually based on only a small extract of an OS map (don't forget to include a title, a key, shading, labelling, etc.).

- When in the field, you may need to 'set' or orientate the map so that your view fits the map view – this can easily be done by turning the map round so that significant features on the map coincide with those on the ground.

- Remember that the map key 'unlocks' the information on the map, some of which may be relevant to your safety. Pay particular attention to the symbols for public footpaths (sometimes confused with parish or other authority boundaries), steep ground, river channels, marshy areas, firing ranges, etc.

- If you are lucky your county LEA may have an OS 'virtual reality' computer package, allowing you to **render** three-dimensional images of urban and rural landscapes anywhere in the UK.

Photographing

Taking your own photographs is an easy way of collecting primary data for a project, and has the advantage of being under your control. Photographing and sketching are both means of recording what you see around you and the resulting snaps and sketches provide both alternative and complementary resources. Photographs are far more than mere space-fillers – vital clues, evidence and information can be extracted from them, and they will add an extra **aesthetic** ingredient to your report. As well as taking your own snaps, look out for old photographs and postcards – these are valuable secondary sources and may provide vital evidence of change over time.

Limitations

- Photos can make a project report look like a glorified photo album particularly when they lack explanation and are disconnected from the text.

- Films take time to process. Many studies are held up at the end because the prints are not ready.

When to photograph

- When time and other circumstances (e.g. a high wind) are against your making a field sketch.

- Where the subject matter is sensitive, fast-moving or short-lived (e.g. a military area, passing traffic).

- When field equipment is being used (e.g. a flowmeter (see page 25-26) or anemometer (see page 52) – to show how it is used and what it looks like.

- When a site is being assessed for safety risks (to provide vital evidence).

- When group work is taking place – to capture group in action (both good and bad practice - Figure 1), and to provide evidence of your involvement in a fieldwork project.

- When it is important to focus on particular details or things that are difficult to sketch (e.g. building or landscape design, plants/animals/people, streetscapes and traffic flows).

- When evidence is needed to support quality or judgement surveys (see pages 42-45).

- To capture unusual light conditions or dramatic events (e.g. silhouettes, rivers in flood, rainbows, stormy seas).

Starting out

- Your camera should be light and not too expensive/valuable – consider the use of a disposable camera.

- Try using a wrist strap for your camera, to reduce the risk of damage or loss. Keep the camera inside your clothing or rucksack, for protection, but make sure it is easily accessible for a 'fast-draw' shot.

- Choose the correct film for the job: 400

Figure 1: Capture the reality of groupwork in action, warts and all.

ASA film for low light conditions, otherwise 100/200 ASA for fast moving objects and/or brighter conditions.

- Colour print films are the most versatile, and a 24-exposure film should be big enough for your needs.

- Get as close to the subject as possible and/or use a zoom lens if you have one.

- Keep a running list of the shots and record the location, subject matter, direction of view, time, date and weather. Alternatively, record this information back at base.

- Be very selective about what pictures you take – one roll of film should be sufficient. If you are involved in group fieldwork and need several sets of photographs, take one set of shots and order multiple copies from the processor –

it is much cheaper that way.

- If light or weather conditions are poor for photographing, don't waste money on taking pictures – poor quality shots can be counterproductive in a report.

ICT links

- If you have access to a digital camera, use it. You can download the pictures onto a computer, and use a photo-editing package to crop, sharpen and enhance them.

- Ordinary prints can be scanned into a computer and manipulated in various ways to alter or improve them. This can include the positioning of labels and annotations.

Bowen, A. and Pallister, J. (1997) *Tackling Geography Coursework*. Hodder & Stoughton, pages 60-61.

Equipment

* Camera and appropriate film, filters, wrist strap, etc. (see 'Starting out')
* Log book • OHP pens
* Corner mounts

How to do it

1. Find a safe, comfortable and sheltered position to take your shot.

2. Be clear in your mind what the purpose of the shot is, and be sure that the main subject of the picture stands out clearly and obviously.

3. Avoid pointing the camera towards bright light, keep the camera still and watch out for your own shadow.

4. If you have a manual camera (i.e. SLR type) rather than an automatic, make sure it is correctly set: exposure, aperture, correct film speed setting, etc. Remember you may need to use a tripod in low light conditions.

Victorian-style post box (in keeping with historic site)

Tudor buildings (pre-1700) converted to pub and shop usage at street level

Georgian brick-built properties (late eighteenth century)

The old Market Hall (made of local sandstone) used until recently as a Magistrate's Court

Statue of Clive of India on granite plinth

Pedestrian zone (paved with replica stone slabs) with varied street furniture, e.g. wooden benches, 'period' litter bin and signposting – part of the process of returning town centres to people

Landscaping elements to 'green' the environment, e.g. trees, wrought-iron planter

People feeding pigeons, encouraging excess numbers and the problem of acidic bird droppings

Figure 2: View of the Market Square, Shrewsbury from the High Street.

Getting the best results

* When ordering prints, go for 6"x4" glossy prints – these are cheaper and use less space than the larger versions.

* Don't be nervous of doctoring your prints (with scissors or on screen – see ICT links) to reshape, reduce or improve them (e.g. by cutting out 'dead space').

* Permanent OHP pens can be used to draw lines on to photographs. In dark areas, white correction fluid can be used instead but it is difficult to do this neatly.

* Use corner mounts rather than adhesive to hold photos in position until you have finalised your report – this allows you to make modifications at a later stage.

* An effective form of presentation is to arrange your prints around a central map, sketch or diagram on an A3 sheet. Contact prints (available with APS and standard 35mm - 7"x5") are good for this because of their small size (5x3cm), but beware illegibility.

* Beside each presented photo, write a title (describing its purpose), a six-figure grid reference (or other locational clue)

and the direction of view. Leave enough space around the photos to label the significant features, processes or issues, and add **annotated** comments to bring out the main 'message' (Figure 2).

* Photos help to bring a report alive and give a 'feel' for places and activities, but you need to be highly selective – steer clear of poor shots, don't overload the text for the sake of it, and make sure each photo has a clear purpose. If there is one shot that summarises a key project aim or issue, consider using it to 'set the scene', either in the introduction or on the cover page.

Figure 3: The site of the Millennium Dome 1985 and 1999. Photos: London Aerial Picture Library.

And finally...

Photographs taken in a series from the same fixed point may be ideal for certain projects, e.g. to show time-lapse changes in traffic volumes, pedestrian densities, low and high tide levels. If you are lucky, and/or have great foresight, you could take before and after shots relating to such things as land use change (e.g. bypass or retail park on **greenfield** or **brownfield sites** - **Figure 3**) or weather effects (e.g. a woodland or park before and after storm damage).

'Photography and field sketches in coursework', *Geography Review*, vol. 12, no. 3, January 1999.

page 61

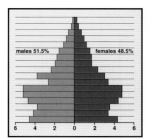

males 51.5%   females 48.5%

P Population Surveys

Over six billion people live on this planet. Nearly 60 million of them in the UK. However, where once people remained in the same area from birth to death, nowadays, they are much more mobile. It is hardly surprising, then, that 'population' (or demography) offers a wide range of study options (some of which are shown in Figure 1). Your population study should identify demographic patterns and trends, relate these to familiar theories and ideas in geography, and explore any issues raise by your findings. An ideal opportunity to use a variety of statistical methods (e.g. percentages, density, indexes, ratios) as well as a mix of presentation.

What's in the population box?

- Population total and density
- Distribution and concentrations
- Percentage change over time
- Age and gender composition
- Marital status and family size
- Fertility/mortality rates
- Ethnic proportions
- Migration patterns
- Life expectancy
- Dependency ratios
- Socio-economic composition

In all of these enquiries you will need the Small Area Statistics (SAS) from the 1991 Census (and earlier ones if appropriate) to guide you on your way. This is a pack of raw data available on microfilm in reference libraries (see samples in Figure 2), but the more consumer-friendly form is the *SCAMP-2* CD-Rom which should be held in most schools/colleges.

The demographic menu

5. Studying the scale and impacts of urban or rural migration

1. A comparative study of population characteristics in two contrasting urban wards or rural parishes

2. A study of changing population features in a given area over time

4. Mapping the distribution and spatial concentration of particular groups of people

3. Mapping and accounting for deprivation/ affluence in a small-scale urban area

Figure 1

Limitations

- Most of the statistics you will handle are derived from Census areas, particularly wards, parishes and enumeration districts. Unfortunately some of these have undergone boundary changes since 1981, making comparisons very difficult between 1981 and 1991.

- You have to be very careful when questioning strangers about personal details such as their age, ethnicity, religion or occupation. Make sure you can present the purpose and context of your enquiries clearly and convincingly.

- It is all too easy for your geography coursework to mutate into a piece of historical research – a common problem in this field of study.

Notes

- For Figure 2a the age bandings are not uniform, and the total population is 416 400.

- For both tables you will have to convert the figures to percentages so that comparisons can be made, e.g. in Figure 2(a), the total number of people with a long-term illness = 11% of the total population.

Figure 2: Typical small area statistics (1991).

(a) Residents in households with limiting long-term illness

Age (years)	Males	Females	Total
0-4	266	192	458
5-15	716	551	1267
16-29	1409	1165	2574
30-44	2406	2213	4619
45-54	2663	2651	5314
55-64	5152	4052	9204
65-74	5408	5897	11 305
76-84	3301	5612	8913
85 & over	701	1952	2653
All ages	22 022	24 265	46 287

(b) Family type and tenure (10% sample)	Owned outright	Buying	Rented privately	Rented from housing association	Rented from local authority	Total households
One person household	1248	757	376	107	1033	3523
Married couple, no children	1616	1496	174	41	538	3865
Married couple, with children	316	2710	164	15	470	3675
Cohabiting couple, no children	52	323	75	2	43	495
Cohabiting couple, with children	8	137	20	4	125	294
Lone parent family	75	231	42	15	304	667

Population change

1-2 DAYS

This focus here is on changes in population size and structure over time in a particular place, e.g. a suburban area or commuter village (this covers items 2 in 5 in Figure 1). This enquiry is only possible if the study area has not undergone significant boundary changes this century (the Census has been taken every decade since 1801).

Steps to take

- Define the study area. Research old 1:10 000 OS maps for the area and create a 'growth' map to show development over time (you can support this with direct observation of the age of buildings - see page 89).

- Draw a line graph to show population totals for successive years and mark on the key events (Figure 4).

'Deprivation and health in Sheffield', *Geography Review*, vol. 13, no. 5, November 1999.

Urban transect

This involves the sampling of two or more wards using an urban **transect** (this covers items 1 and 4 in Figure 1). The aims of the study are:

1. To investigate the **socio-economic** variations within a large built-up area, and to relate this to urban models and theories. The obvious approach is to compare an inner-city with a suburban ward.

2. To compare primary data (gathered in the field) with information gained from secondary sources (e.g. SAS and cartographic images from the SCAMP database) and to discuss the value and limitations of each source.

Steps to take

1. Obtain an outline map of the urban wards – this can be printed off from the SCAMP CD (the wards can be identified by name and coding by referring to the 'boundary key' file in SCAMP), for example, Handsworth ward in Birmingham is encoded O7CNFL.

2. Decide upon your line of transect – it should cross as many different types of ward as possible (Figure 3).

3. Your sampling points should be stratified within each ward – as close to the mid-point of the transect - so long as this location is a typical residential area (you will need a detailed street map).

4. In terms of primary data gathering you can:

- Undertake a house age and type survey (see page 89 and Appendix) noting down evidence of flats, multi-occupancy, sheltered accommodation, **individualisation**. Take (discrete) photographs. Check out the relative house values and sizes from high street estate agents.

- Carry out an environmental evaluation (see page 43) .

- Survey and record the provision of residential parking, size of gardens, presence of security alarms, etc.

- Carry out pedestrian and/or vehicle surveys on the main streets and on typical residential streets (see pages 14 and 82-84).

- Use questionnaire surveys to assess residents' perceptions of their environment and its desirability (see pages 90-91).

- Research the council tax valuation banding (A-H) to see which ones are typical for each study area, and check the league tables for GCSE results of the nearest local school (percentage of students gaining five or more subjects at grades A-C).

- Calculate the population density per

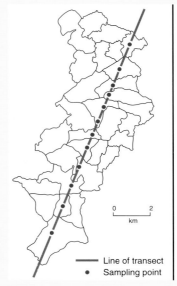

Figure 3: Sampling points on a transect through urban wards.

hectare using SAS data (you may have to work out the area yourself).

- Construct and analyse representative **population pyramids** for each ward.

- Use the SCAMP database to produce socio-economic choropleth maps using key demographic criteria, e.g. unemployment levels, car ownership, long-term ill-health, social grouping.

This type of enquiry has a solid balance of primary and secondary information sources and allows you to discuss the limitations of each.

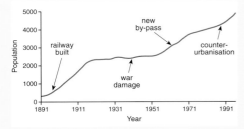

Figure 4: Example of a population graph: 1891-1991.

- Use the SAS to construct two population pyramids to demonstrate (with luck!) the changing demographic structure in your study area (e.g. reduced birth rates, increased life expectancies). This demographic change over time can be further explored using a range of calculations:

Gender ratio: $\dfrac{\text{no. of males}}{\text{no. of females}} \times 100$

Age ratio: $\dfrac{\text{no. of people} >65}{\text{total population}} \times 100$

or $\dfrac{\text{no. of people} <16 \text{ years}}{\text{total population}} \times 100$

Index of ageing: $\dfrac{\text{adults} >65 \text{ years}}{\text{young people} <16 \text{ years}} \times 100$

the more this figure exceeds 100, the increasingly aged or 'greying' the population

Index of fertility: $\dfrac{\text{no. of children} <5 \text{ years}}{\substack{\text{no. of women of}\\ \text{reproductive age}\\ (16\text{-}44 \text{ inclusive})}} \times 1000$

- Consult **Electoral Registers** (see, for example, Figure 5) over a five-year period in the past and a more recent five-year period and note changes in occupancy of properties. This will give an insight into changes in residential stability.

- Conduct a questionnaire survey of heads of households (use drop-and-collect) on a 5-10% sample strategy if possible. The

aim of the survey is to enable you to analyse 'changes over time' with reference to variables such as the age, ethnicity, length of residence and reasons for movement of respondents.

1990	House no.	1995	House no.
Tullis, James	1	Tullis, James	1
Tullis, Catherine	1	Tullis, Catherine	1
Shepherd, Stephen	2	Shepherd, Stephen	2
Shepherd, Beverly	2	Shepherd, Beverley	2
Salter, Wilhelmina	3	Hall, Myfanwy	3
McNeill, William	4	McNeill, Dorothy	4
McNeill, Dorothy	4	Cartwright, Derek	5
Jones, Kevin	5	Cartwright, Janet	5
Downing, Jan	6	Aston, Caroline	6
Downing, Julie	6	Speller, Brian	7
Speller, Brian	7	Ewense, Mark	8
Smalley, Tony	8	Ewense, Kathryn	8
Wheatley, Josephine	9	Plank, Raymond	9
Bradnam, Doris	9	Plank, Christine	9
Unoccupied	10	Peckham, Linda	10

Figure 5: An extract from the Electoral Registers for 1990 and 1995. Note: Over this five-year period, six out of the ten houses have seen a change of occupants.

'The geography of age', *Geography Review*, vol. 7, no. 3, January 1994.

Questionnaires

Questionnaires are very useful devices for finding out about specific groups of people and they are widely used in the commercial world by professional agencies, especially for market research (e.g. MORI, Gallup, National Shoppers Surveys). Questionnaires are also used extensively in AS and A2-level investigations as sources of primary data. However, according to Examiners they are often badly designed and delivered, and often show little progression from GCSE level. While apparently easy, quick and cheap to use, in reality questionnaires present a serious challenge and need to be thought through very carefully if they are to be effective – so don't think they are an easy option!

What is a questionnaire?

A questionnaire is a set of pre-arranged questions designed to obtain information from people about themselves and their views. It is simply a type of form that is specifically useful for collecting current information about local issues, etc., and for assessing people's attitudes and opinions (data not generally available from any other source).

They are ideal for collecting the following types of data:

- basic sociological characteristics of a sample population (e.g. age, gender, occupation)

- **spatial** patterns (e.g. origin of visitors to an area, typical travel pathways in a working day)

- patterns of behaviour (e.g. shopping habits, motives/preferences concerning travel to work and recreational activities).

Questionnaires are also useful for finding out how local, regional or national issues might effect people, e.g. the range and strength of feelings towards the proposed development of a young offenders' institution in a local area.

Limitations

- The problem of 'questionnaire fatigue' – most people are either fed up with or just not interested in responding to questionnaires, whether in the street, on the doorstep or by post.

- Research suggests that people are economical with the truth in surveys and opinion polls. They often respond with an answer that 'sounds' good, or what they think the interviewer wants to hear.

Photo: Elizabeth Rynne.

'Designing questionnaires and interviews', *Geography Review*, vol. 13, no. 1, September 1999.

Different question types

- Closed questions provide the **respondent** with a choice of answer, generally from a directed list. Interviewees are asked to tick the relevant box(es), or to score or rank the items according to their personal preference.

- Open questions are usually 'interview style' questions which tend to be longer. Respondents do not have to make forced choices, i.e. they need not provide answers according to predetermined categories.

How many to use

In general, the more people you can survey the better, but you need to consider the importance of the questionnaire-derived data to your particular study. A minimum of 50 and a maximum of 100 is about right.

In many cases a 10% sample of the population is ideal. For example, in a study of travel-to-work patterns in a large village (population of about 2700 = roughly 1000 houses), this would yield a sample size of 100 houses, which is feasible – but remember that you will still need to think carefully about which 100 houses you will sample. Will you do this at random, or systematically (say every tenth house), or stratified (if half the houses are semi-detached, then make sure that 50 of these are sampled)?

"I've learnt from bitter experience that things don't always go according to plan – like stupid answers to questions, or no answers at all. And as for asking people on the street, it's very difficult to get them interested in my survey. I wonder why?"

Types of questionnaire

Face-to-face:
These are interview-style questionnaires, usually carried out in the street or local neighbourhood, or on the doorstep. Questions are generally closed, requiring only short responses.

Drop-and-collect or delivery/collection:
This involves delivering (or posting in some instances) the questionnaires with an official covering letter, and either collecting the completed copies or having them returned by mail. This type of approach is serviceable if your area is small enough for you to cover easily on foot, or on a bike/car/bus. However, the rate of return will probably be less than 25%, and is likely to be even lower – say 5-10%.

Hints and tips

- For 'drop-and-collect' questionnaires, keep the design clear, simple and easy to follow – respondents can be put off by complex layouts or too many questions.

- Use simple language and follow a few basis rules, as follows:
  - use short words and questions;
  - avoid double negatives (e.g. 'Do you disagree that geography students should not be made to work too hard?' –'should not' is confusing in this case);
  - try not to start with, 'Do you agree that ...', as it begs a 'Yes' answer.
  - avoid any ambiguity in the question, otherwise the answers may not fit your needs;
  - decide if what you want is a person's unbiased view, or if their attitudes are more important.

- Avoid questions which require a lot of thinking about (for example, asking shoppers whether prices are rising faster now than they did ten years ago, or asking people to make estimates involving percentages or fractions).

- Avoid questions which might cause offence where, for example, age, gender, race, culture, religion and income are involved.

  - Do not assume people can supply accurate details (e.g. the distance they have travelled), or that they are well informed about topical issues (e.g. genetically modified foods).

Equipment

- Clipboard and pen/pencil
- Appropriate clothes
- Identification badge and/or official letter from school
- Copies of blank questionnaires

5-10 MINS PER QUESTIONNAIRE (IF ON-STREET), HALF-DAY (DROP AND COLLECT), PLUS HALF DAY FOR DESIGN

How to do it

Design
(See Figures 1 and 2 overleaf)

1. Make sure the questionnaire is the best or only way to collect the data – you may be overlooking sources of secondary data.

2. Decide what you need to know and list all the components of information you need (5-10 questions should be sufficient).

3. Decide on question type (open or closed) and check wording of each question. Keep language simple.

4. Write questions onto cards or use a computer to list them, then sort them into a sensible order.

5. Determine how responses will be recorded, e.g. check boxes, circling preferences or ranking answers.

6. Consider layout and design – try to fit onto one page of A4 only. You can use margins for coding answers. This will reduce photocopy time and cost.

Delivery

- Decide when and where you are going to conduct the questionnaire. This will depend on the nature of your research questions and **hypotheses**. Will it be 'face-to-face', or 'drop-and-collect'?

- Decide on the best sampling strategy. A stratified sample is necessary if you want to sample all parts of the community, i.e. a proportion of men and women, the old and the young, high and low income groups, etc.

- Decide on your target sample size – this will depend on the population and the time available.

A car park in south Shropshire

In this example, a questionnaire-based survey is to be conducted in the car park at a popular tourist spot in the South Shropshire Hills. The site has toilets, a café and visitor information facilities, but the access road is narrow. Recently, the car park has come under threat of closure due to objections from the local community and the parish council relating to congestion of local roads, noise and verge-side parking. The local authority have surveyed the site and estimate that it is visited by approximately 100 000 cars per year, with 75% of visits being in the period between June and August.

Hello, I am a sixth-form student on an A-level course looking at visitors in South Shropshire. I want to ask you some questions.

1. Why have you come here?
2. Have you been here before?
   ☐ Yes ☐ No ☐ Can't remember ☐ Don't know
3. How long do you intend to stay here?
   ☐ Less than a day ☐ Several days ☐ Week
4. Are you aware that you are contributing to the deterioration of this site?
5. Where have you come from?
6. How did you get here?
   ☐ Car ☐ Train ☐ Coach

Figure 1: An example of poor practice.

In Q2, two of the responses are too similar.

In Q3, the responses are not precise enough.

Q4 could be seen as offensive – it implies that the respondent is personally responsible for damage to the site.

This simple non-directed question would be a good one to start with.

In Q6 an 'Other' category should be included in the responses.

Good morning/afternoon. I am an A-level geography student from Preston Montford Field Centre in Shrewsbury. I want to conduct a survey of visitors and I would value your opinion. Would you mind answering some questions? It won't take more than a few minutes.

1. Have you ever visited this site before? ☐ yes ☐ no

2. How did you come to hear about his place?
   ☐ advert/flier ☐ saw on TV ☐ newspaper ☐ friend ☐ already knew ☐ other

3. How far have you travelled to get here today?
   ☐ 5km ☐ <6-20km ☐ 21-30km ☐ >30km

4. If you did not arrive here by car, how did you travel to the site? (indicate all that might apply)
   ☐ bus/coach ☐ walking ☐ bicycle ☐ motorbike ☐ train ☐ other

5. What are your reasons for visiting? (indicate all that might apply)
   ☐ dog walking ☐ visiting friends ☐ running/jogging ☐ sightseeing (little walking)
   ☐ walking >2km ☐ picnicking ☐ mountain biking ☐ to use facilities ☐ take a rest
   ☐ education/scientific ☐ for the children ☐ nostalgic ☐ other (please specify) ....

6. If you had more time here could you rank what your main preference would be from the list on the previous question? ☐ dog walking ☐ visiting friends
   ☐ running/jogging ☐ sightseeing ☐ walking ☐ picnicking ☐ mountain biking
   ☐ facilities ☐ take a rest ☐ education ☐ children ☐ nostalgic ☐ other

7. How long do you intend to stay (a) at this site? (b) in the area?
   ☐ <1 hour ☐ 1-2 hours ☐ 2-4 hours ☐ >4 hours ☐ 1 day ☐ 1-2 days ☐ 2-4 days ☐ longer

8. Are you aware of any problems with this site? If so, what? ....

9. This is considered to be an attractive site. How far do you agree with this?
   ☐ Strongly agree ☐ Agree ☐ Haven't considered it ☐ Disagree ☐ Strongly disagree

10. Could you give me your postcode? ....

☐ male ☐ female   ☐ <20 ☐ 20-35 ☐ 36-50 ☐ 51-65 ☐ >65

Time and date .... Weather .... Survey no. ....
Thank you for your time. All of this information will be treated as confidential. Goodbye.

Figure 2: An example of sound practice. (Can you say why this is better than Figure 1?)

Use a first sentence as an introduction to approach people. Do not forget to explain why you want their help and why you value it.

Open with some easy, non-sensitive closed questions to 'warm up' and relax the respondent.

Always include 'other' categories for multiple-answer questions.

The questionnaire shows a progression - starting with simple closed questions and building towards more open and structured responses. Question 6 is an example of a ranked relative preference.

Question 8 is an example of an open question. Make sure you leave enough room for the response.

Question 9 is an example of a 'Likert scal question – good for attitudes and opinions.

The postcode is a very useful piece of information with which to work out exact locations.

Avoid asking personal questions directly. You can make an informed judgement yourself.

Bowen, A. and Pallister, J. (1997) *Tackling Geography Coursework.* Hodder & Stoughton, pages 18-21.

Other design issues regarding the questionnaire shown in Figure 1

1. Poor question sequencing, e.g. Q1 is open-ended and possibly discursive so is best left for the end.
2. Generally, there is a lack of directed responses, e.g. Q1 could have had several response options.
3. The format of the responses for Q1, Q4 and Q5 means that data analysis will be difficult.

Tips on sampling

- Conduct a pilot study with a small sample of respondents (10-20 people). Watch out for 'uncomfortable' questions or any which may be misinterpreted, and choose a sequence which is both logical and maintains interest. Ensure that the questionnaire will take no longer than five minutes to complete.

- A minimum sample of 10% of the target population is ideal. In the Shropshire car park example, given the known figures about numbers of visitors, if the survey was being carried out in late August you would expect over 800 cars per day, i.e.

$$\frac{75\,000}{92\ (\text{days})} = 815 \text{ cars per day.}$$

A 10% sample would therefore be around 80 cars.

- In the Shropshire example, it would be useful to take account of:

a) variations in the number of cars over time, e.g. weekends and weekdays, as well as mornings and afternoons;

b) the average stay of cars; the average number of people per car; the number of empty car parking spaces.

Photo: Paula Richardson.

And finally ...

Cross tabulation is a useful technique to use if you think that two or more categories of information are related. Figure 3 is an example based on data collected from the Shropshire case study. Here, the age of the respondents is one category, and the activity/reason for their visit is the other. As you can see, certain patterns have emerged: e.g. most people in the age category 20-35 have visited the site to go walking for a distance of more than two kilometres. Additional information (e.g. gender) could be added to the basic categories by colour coding the tallies, thus revealing more patterns. The use of databases and spreadsheets will help in this process.

Your questionnaire could ask respondents to create a mental map by adding information to a base map supplied by you (see 'Judgement Surveys', page 45). This will test their spatial awareness and familiarity with the given study site. In the Shropshire case, the map could cover the access road, the site itself, and the **amenities,** and the respondents could be asked to mark potential conflict points with an X.

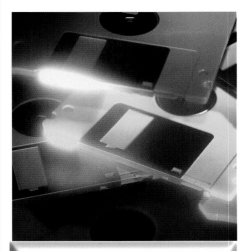

ICT links

- Try to word-process all of your questionnaires and covering letters. As well as looking more professional, the end result will fill less space than a hand-written version so you can fit far more questions/directed responses on to one page.

- You might be able to record the answers to closed questions in a simple spreadsheet. This will make analysis easier, especially if you are intending to make statistical **correlations** (Figure 3).

- If appropriate, you might consider delivering/collecting your questionnaires using e-mail.

Activity \ Age	<20	21-35	36-50	51-65	>65	Totals
Dog walking	I	I	IIII	IIII	II	12
Visiting friends			III	II		5
Running/jogging	I	I	I			3
Sightseeing		I	IIII	IIII II	IIII	17
Walking >2km		IIII IIII II	IIII II	IIII	II	25
Picnicking	II		II			4
Mountain biking	IIII II		I			8
Use facilities	II		I	IIII	IIII	13
Take a rest	I					1
Education, etc.	IIII I					6
For the children			II			2
Nostalgic			I			1
Other (specified)						0
Totals	20	15	26	22	14	

Figure 3: Example cross-tabulation.

Robinson, G.M. (1988) *Methods and Techniques in Human Geography.* John Wiley, pages 377-94.

Risk Assessment

Assessing and managing risk are life skills which can be applied in most aspects of decision making. In the context of coursework projects in the field, risk assessment and management are an essential part of the work you need to do (and you won't need any specialist equipment or skills). By taking steps to protect the well being of yourself and all those involved, you will be demonstrating maturity and concern for others – attributes not lost on the Examiners! Even if no marks are offered for risk assessment as such, you can still strengthen the planning aspect of your work by including it. You might also use risk assessment techniques as part of a **qualitative** study on 'risk perception' in relation to selected sites (see Extension ideas opposite).

When to use

Risk assessment helps you to realise there are many potential problems associated with fieldwork. This approach should be applied to all types of environment, ranging from suburbs to sand dunes, motorways to moorland, regardless of how 'safe' they may seem (see 'Fieldwork Safety' on page 9).

Definitions

Hazard: this is anything that has the potential to do you, or others, harm. For example, hypothermia is a potential hazard associated with working in an upland environment, and traffic accidents are a potential hazard associated with transport surveys in a town.

Risk: is the actual chance or probability (high or low) that someone will be harmed by the hazard.

Steps to take

The model used by the Government's Health and Safety Executive is a useful one to follow when carrying out your own risk assessment:

1. Look for and identify hazards.

2. Decide who might be harmed and how.

3. Evaluate the risks and decide whether existing controls or precautions are adequate or if more are needed. Ask yourself:

   a) Can I get rid of the hazard altogether (e.g. remove a broken branch)?

   b) If not, how can I control the risk so that the possibility of harm is unlikely/minimised?

4. Record the findings (Figure 1).

5. Review the assessment and revise if necessary.

Figure 2: Surely there is risk here? Sheep attack!

Hints and tips

- Not all potential hazards will be obvious to you (Figure 2) so it is worth working with friends to share ideas about the risks attached to your chosen project and field sites. Be imaginative, and think of others in your group as well as yourself (e.g. some may fear heights).

- Keep things simple and seek guidance from your teacher when starting the assessment process.

Limitations

- The assessment is based on a value judgement made by you which, given that you have only limited experience, means it could be unreliable.

- It is easy to become obsessive about risk assessment and to get it out of all proportion such that it dominates coursework reports, suggesting even that fieldwork is too risky to attempt.

SITE SPECIFIC RISK ASSESSMENT

Site/area ....

Grid reference .... 1:25 000 sheet number ....

Potential hazards ....

....

Action to be taken ....

....

Nearest telephone ....

Emergency contact number (for school/college) ....

Figure 1: Example hazard card.

 'Risky work', *Geography Review*, vol. 12, no. 4, March 1999.

Speech bubbles within image:
- Would you stand here?
- Severity of outcome due to the fall potential = 4 (major injury leading to hospitalisation). Cliffs do not have to be steep to be dangerous.
- Likelihood of falling over the cliff = 2 (may occur, but very rarely). The students are mostly lying down – but is this really safe?

Photo: Tim Burt.

Figure 3: Risk assessment of a cliff-top location.

Extension ideas

1. Why not use the risk assessment model as a qualitative technique for assessing risk perception in a town centre? Mark potential survey sites on a map and give each one a risk score. Do this for different times of the day (and night) and different days of the week.

2. Investigate how and why different people perceive risk in different ways (e.g. are the differences related to such things as age, gender or familiarity with an area?). You can use the same scoring system as shown here.

A score of 8 (2 x 4) has been given to the example shown in Figure 3. This means the activity is acceptable and carries only slight risk. While the activity appears to be well managed, is it really an example of good practice?

Strategies for different situations

A. Working in streams and small rivers

1. Evaluate the site – carry out a site visit.

2. Establish who owns the river banks and check if anyone has fishing rights – seek permission.

3. Identify points of access to sites and assess them for potential hazards (e.g. thorny bushes, steep muddy ground, deep pools, slippery rocks, boulders).

4. Contact the Environment Agency (especially if working in urban areas) to check if there is any danger of contracting Weil's disease (the incidence is usually very low – see 'Water Quality Surveys' page 96).

5. Tape all cuts and wear rubber gloves in streams with **pollution** potential, e.g. from silage liquor or sewage.

6. Check the weather reports for the **catchment area** for the 12/24hr period prior to a field visit, in case of a rapid increase in water levels.

B. Working in the built environment

In urban areas there is a higher probability of 'psychological' hazards being encountered than in the countryside – i.e. people becoming upset and abusive. This can happen during interviews, for example, or when taking photographs of houses or street scenes. The following measures should be considered as part of your risk management strategy in such areas:

- Introduce yourself to the managers of supermarkets, shops and malls and seek their permission to conduct surveys, etc.

- Carry an 'official' (i.e. school/college) clipboard if you have one, and a letter from your group leader/Head of Geography Department explaining what you are doing. A student card with photograph is also worth taking with you.

- Decide in advance on a 'low risk' protocol for approaching and questioning people, and recording information.

Likelihood of occurrence
1. Highly unlikely ever to occur
2. May occur but very rarely
3. Does occur but only rarely
4. Occurs sometimes
5. Likely to occur often

Severity of outcome
1. Slight inconvenience
2. Minor injury requiring first aid
3. Medical attention required
4. Major injury leading to hospitalisation
5. Fatal or serious injury leading to disability

Risk = Likelihood x Severity

A score of >10 indicates that the risk needs to be managed. Have a look at Figure 3 – do you agree with the score?

'Fieldwork and risk management', *Teaching Geography*, vol. 25, no. 2, April 2000.

page 69

Rural Enquiries

Rural environments in the UK range from urban **Green Belts** to remote wildernesses. Taken together they occupy a much higher proportion of the land area than urban environments, though the balance is shifting, particularly in the Midlands and south east of England. While agriculture remains the dominant activity in rural areas, there is increasing pressure from a range of competing land uses, especially at the rural-urban fringe (e.g. retail and business parks, housing and industrial estates, and golf courses). Such land uses are 'pulled' towards rural locations by lower land prices, higher environmental quality and freedom from urban congestion. The consequence of these and other developments has been a dramatic shift in the character and functioning of many rural settlements.

Dorrington, Shropshire: an example

This example is typical of many 'rural' coursework projects and illustrates the potential of groupwork in the gathering of both primary and secondary data. The exercise is designed for a party of 12-16 students on the new AS/A2 **specification** courses, the final outcome being a 2-3000 word report, with each student taking responsibility for their own title and **hypothesis**, data processing, presentation, analysis and conclusion.

The Ordnance Survey map extract (Figure 1) is of a rural, largely agricultural area, approximately 10km south of Shrewsbury (Figure 2). The village of

Equipment
- **Large-scale** Ordnance Survey map of area
- Recording sheets, questionnaires
- **Small area statistics** • Camera

SEE INDIVIDUAL SUB-SECTIONS

Dorrington (population 450 in 1991) lies on the busy A49 trunk road which links industrial Lancashire with South Wales.

10. Land use mapping to identify changes over the last 20 yrs – conflict **matrix**?

11. What evidence is there of urban influences, including the impact of the new A5 bypass?

12. Possible river study – channel **variables**, flood risk, meanders, etc.

1. Quarrying (sand and gravel) – an impact study of past and present workings

2. Bypass proposal – an evaluation of two options including environmental impact assessments (EIAs)

9. Comparative village study – Stapleton and Dorrington

8. Traffic survey to determine the impact of the A49(T) on Dorrington, including evaluation of traffic calming measures

7. Footpath **transect** (2km) to survey land use on either side (20 fields), route quality assessment and possibly hedge/woodland studies

3. Farm study – single or comparative, changing patterns of land use

4. Public transport provision for Dorrington, including a **feasibility** survey concerning the re-opening of the railway station

5. Demographic study of Dorrington over the last 50-100 years, including building, functional and employment changes

6. Service and amenity provision study, including issues and **catchment areas**

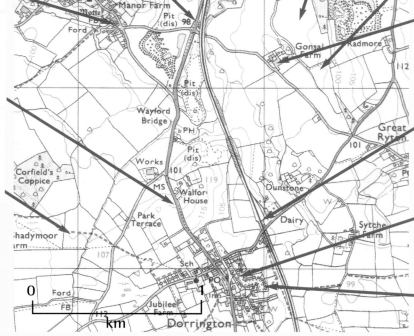

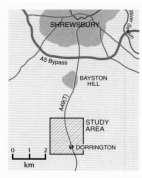

Figure 1 (above): Areas for possible study around Dorrington area. Mapping reproduced from Ordnance Survey 1:25 000 Pathfinder mapping with permission of The Controller of Her Majesty's Stationery Office © Crown Copyright. Licence number MC100030715. Figure 2 (left): The location of the study area shown in Figure 1.

Doomsday Project – Interactive BBC video disk, available in most main libraries. It includes a partial UK survey (mid-1980s) of agricultural land use.

Getting started

The umbrella (or general) question might be: 'In what ways is Dorrington a typical rural settlement?' The steps to be taken in planning and conducting an enquiry might be as follows:

1. A two-hour reconnaissance of the area by the whole group. Students to be dropped off in pairs at pre-determined sites to evaluate the viability of fieldwork in the area.

2. Each pair devises an enquiry theme (see points 1-12 on Figure 1) and then develops this into a title, statement or question, involving a pattern, **relationship** or issue. For example:

   - An investigation into the traffic issue posed by the A49 trunk road through Dorrington.

   - 'How has the demographic and commercial change in Dorrington reflected its status as a proposed **key settlement?**'

   - 'Economic and behavioural **factors** have a stronger influence on agricultural land usage than physical factors.'

3. Each pair produces an outline strategy for data collection (possibly commenting on the feasibility of this, using a scale of 1-5, where 0 = a non-starter).

4. A small research group does a library search for aerial photographs, for agricultural and transport data, and for data from **Electoral Registers**, **Census** returns and parish records.

Later on

2-3 LESSONS

1. Within two weeks of fieldwork and research visits to the area, students prepare a report-back and discussion session (allowing time for film processing, report planning and **pilot surveys**). Each pair makes a five-minute presentation supported by visual aids (e.g. flip chart, photographs, artefacts, OHTs). The research group provides basic facts about the area, including a description of the site, situation and (brief) history of Dorrington.

2. A further exercise would be required to allow the whole group to produce a generic questionnaire survey (Figure 3) and to decide on an appropriate sampling strategy for it.

Site saturation: pros and cons

Sites such as Dorrington are attractive for student fieldwork projects, so there is a danger that they become 'over-studied', which may lead to **plagiarism** and possibly resentment on the part of people who live in the study area. However, if the studies were made once every three years and rotated with studies of contrasting environments (e.g. urban, coastal), a useful database could be built up.

---

1. Which of the following age categories do you fit into?
   ☐ under 30   ☐ 30-44   ☐ 45-59   ☐ 60 and over

2. How long have you lived in this area (not necessarily this house)? _____ years.

3. a) Where is your place of work? _____
   b) How do you usually get there? _____

4. On a daily basis, do you have access to a car?
   ☐ always   ☐ sometimes   ☐ infrequently   ☐ rarely/never

1. Rank the three major problems of living in Dorrington from the options below, where 1 = worst.

   Note: Options to be listed here will vary according to the area and might include, for example, crime and vandalism, traffic noise, house prices, lack of shops.

6. How effective have the traffic calming measures been in Dorrington?
   ☐ Very   ☐ Moderately   ☐ Ineffective

7. Roughly what proportion of your weekly shopping bill is spent in local shops?
   _____

8. Would you use the railway station at Dorrington if it was re-opened
   ☐ Yes   ☐ No   ☐ Unsure

   Note: Additional information on the age and type of each house can be collected as a separate part of the fieldwork exercise.

This questionnaire has been put together by a group of sixth-form geography students from Scarecrow College in Shrewsbury. We are investigating various elements of rural life in the Dorrington area, and we would greatly appreciate it if you would respond to the questions below. We are sending out 100 questionnaires and need a 50% return rate to make our enquiries worthwhile. We will collect them between 6pm and 7pm in two days' time. If you will be out at that time, could you please leave your completed copy on the doorstep. The results will remain confidential. Thank you for your time.

Figure 3: A sample questionnaire, linked to the Dorrington case study.

'Exploring the rural past', *Geography Review*, vol. 6, no. 4, March 1993.

page **71**

Getting it done

What follows are examples of how some of the themes listed in Figure 1 might be developed. Some will work better than others, but all form the basis of meaningful and manageable AS/A2-level investigations. Some of these have the potential for use by GCSE students.

Quarrying

Beware the trap of over-exaggerating the negative impact of quarries and open-cast mines – they may only be short-term, and of small scale, and some people might feel that they are of real economic benefit to the area. Be sure to keep an open mind.

1. Sketch the quarry workings, including buildings, storage and waste heaps. Note the rock type(s) and structure, and mark on access roads, nearby houses and settlements and adjacent land uses.

2. Contact the local planning authority for details of the extraction licence for the quarry (its extent and duration) and find out what, if any, agreement was made about what will happen to the land after quarrying ceases. Relate the location and size of the workings to the nearest centres of population.

3. Locate points in various directions around the quarry at distances of 1-8km. Visit these sites by road and foot and evaluate the view of the quarry from each one (score 0 if it is not visible, score 1 if it is barely noticeable or blends in, and score 5 if it is very obtrusive and ugly). You could use the same sites to investigate noise pollution from the quarry, but you will need to take the prevailing wind direction into account (see 'Air Quality Assessment', page 17).

4. Survey the access and local roads (their width, quarry dust and vehicle damage etc.) and conduct quarry traffic surveys (size and frequency of vehicles) as the basis for studies of the suitability of the roads for lorry traffic, and dust and/or noise pollution.

5. Arrange a questionnaire survey on a drop-and-collect basis at nearby farms and houses (see page 65). These should explore strength of feelings concerning blasting or machinery noise, vibration damage, air-borne dust and lorry traffic. Research local newspapers for articles and readers' letters relating to the quarry.

6. Try to arrange an interview with the quarry manager to obtain details of production rates, main markets, numbers of employees (and whether or not they live locally, i.e. within 8km of the quarry), and any precautions taken against pollution and disturbance.

Quarrying is an essential primary industry providing employment and a range of useful materials. It has to take place somewhere (despite the NIMBY syndrome). Disused quarries can, over time, provide wildlife habitats (particularly where shallow lakes form), and recreational resources (e.g. bird watching, water sports, rock climbing).

Bypass surveys

Shropshire County Council considered diverting the A49(T) around Dorrington using a short section of bypass. It is unlikely that this option will go ahead because of budgetary constraints. Your job is to research the original plans and proposals, including the up-dated costings. Mark the optional routes on your base map and conduct an environmental impact assessment of both (see pages 32-33). You could also put forward your own proposal and justify it.

Points to consider:
- Length of bypass
- Purchase of land
- Number of houses to be compensated within 200m impact zone
- Disruption to traffic flows during construction
- Disruption to farm holdings, e.g. moving livestock
- Impact on local habitats and wildlife
- Loss of passing trade to Dorrington
- Additional construction costs due to gradients, poorly drained areas, crossing rivers/railways.

Set against these costs are the potential benefits: local employment and service opportunities, smoother traffic flows, and a return to a fairly peaceful, cleaner and safer village environment.

For traffic surveys including traffic calming measures, see 'Transport Surveys' pages 82-87. In the case of Dorrington these measures have provided a solution at a much lower cost than the proposed bypass, though they have not solved the problem of heavy traffic flows.

Settlement surveys

These could deal with demographic change (see 'Population Surveys' pages 62-63), change in the built environment, service and amenity provision, and settlement spacing and hierarchies. You can either focus on a single settlement, or you can compare two of a similar size (note that Census population data is at the parish not village level, and remember parish boundaries have changed over time). You can either count the total number of houses in the settlement and multiply by 2.8 (known as the family multiplier) or, for more accurate figures, contact the local authority or County Council planning departments.

To calculate population change over time (50 years):

$$\frac{\text{population for 1981}}{\text{population for 1931}} \times 100 = \% \text{ change}$$

To study change over time in the built environment, map the current extent of the settlement and compare this with past extents using old maps (see 'Urban Enquiries' page 88). Also produce a simplified land use map of the settlement using the same categories as those used in 'Urban Enquiries'.

The land use map will show service and amenity provision. You can evaluate the quality and suitability of this provision (e.g. in Dorrington, with a population of only 450, you would expect only low-order services (church, pub, post office and only basic amenities (children's play area, village hall)). Any anomalies in the expected pattern should be commented upon (e.g. Dorrington was originally designated a key settlement with planning approval for expansion to service outlying hamlets – therefore you would expect it to have higher order services).

To study settlement spacing, obtain population figures for the whole district or county and construct a rank-size graph. You can also work out average spacings between settlements of similar size, and compare this to geographical models.

Farm surveys

These enquiries are not really achievable without the co-operation of the farmer or farm manager – they are only effective if done by students who have farming connections. All farmed areas in the UK are classified on a scale of 1-5 according to their physical characteristics: altitude, slope, exposure, annual rainfall, and soil quality (depth, acidity, organic content and drainage). (See the Land Capability table in the Appendix page 106).

1. **Delimit** the farm holding on a base map at a scale of 1:10 000 where all field boundaries are shown. Broadly categorise the land use in each field using the Land Utilisation Key in the Appendix, e.g. cereals. These surveys work best in spring

Estimate the relative percentages of these categories (e.g. in your study, woodland

might occupy 10% of the farm holding).

to early autumn. Take along binoculars where access is limited, and a camera for taking photos as evidence of land use, livestock type, field enlargement and any environmental initiatives (e.g. organic farming, woodland shelter and **field headlands** (good for barn-owls).

2. Decide upon the capability class of each field (highly productive arable land is class 1, e.g. East Anglian Fens). With permission, support this evaluation by undertaking surveys in a few selected fields: slope, soil quality and infiltration rates (see 'Soil Surveys' on pages 80-81). From these sample surveys you can determine the extent and strength of the connection between physical factors and field usage.

3. Using a detailed farm map, or an aerial photograph, make a sketch of the farmyard and buildings, labelling their **functions** (e.g. machinery shed). At this point you should consider whether there is any longer a relationship between what is produced in a field and its distance from the farmhouse.

4. Devise either a questionnaire or a set of interview questions and arrange a time slot convenient to the farmer. You need to address the following points (avoid asking questions about the operational costs and profits):
   - Size of the farm (**hectares**)
   - Type of **tenure**
   - Age of farmer
   - Labour (full-time/part-time or contract)
   - Capital equipment
   - Livestock numbers and type
   - Crop yields (in what seasons grown?)
   - Facts and figures concerning inputs: fertilisers, pesticides/herbicides, fuel, stock feed, vet. services, seed stock, drainage/irrigation systems, heating, etc. (ideally, expressed as rough percentages of the total operational costs).
   - Available subsidies/grants (possibly as a percentage of total farm income)
   - Storage facilities, methods of **distribution**, and markets for the outputs
   - The main problems of farming in the last decade:
     General: 1) ....
             2) ....
             3) ....
     Specific: 1) ....
              2) ....
              3) ....
   - The political impacts of European Union (Common Agricultural Policy)

- Finally, compare the changing pattern of past and present land uses (see page 104). Past maps may reveal field enlargement and hedgerow removal to promote mechanisation and intensification. The farmer may hold

and UK (Ministry of Agriculture Fisheries and Food) agricultural policies.
- Environmental initiatives undertaken and difficulties encountered
- Economic diversification (with comments on viability)
- The farmer's values (score 0 if irrelevant, score 3 if essential, score 1 or 2 if intermediate)
Healthy outdoor lifestyle ☐
Maintaining the farm traditions ☐
Independence ☐
Modernisation (technical improvements) ☐
Maximising income ☐
Working with animals ☐
Challenging occupation ☐
Able to influence farming policies and market prices ☐
Flexible working hours ☐
Passing the farm into the family ☐
Satisfaction of producing healthy food ☐
The weather ☐
Being an environmental caretaker ☐
Other? ☐

Note: These value responses will vary according to the farm tenure and size, the farmer's age, background and education, and the land quality. Such surveys can work well when two farms with similar physical characteristics are compared, particularly when the land use is significantly different, and the farmers have different outlooks on life.

farm records and land use maps dating back at least 30 years – you may be able to put together a revealing account of change (including buildings) influenced by political, economic and behavioural decisions.

'Farmers, farming and land-use', *Geography Review*, vol. 11, no. 2, November 1997.

page **73**

Sampling Techniques

Life is too short for you to gather all the information you need in order to make decisions and conclusions. So you will probably use sampling techniques instead. This will apply to nearly all geographical coursework you undertake so it is worth spending time to learn how to do it well. Appropriate and well considered sampling decisions should lead to quality primary data gathering which will have a cascade effect through the whole report – though no matter how good the sampling strategy, it is a waste of time if your measurements and procedures in the field are sloppy and inaccurate.

A sample is a small part or fragment of a whole to represent what the whole picture is really like. The larger the sample, the more accurate the representation should be. The whole picture is termed the 'sampling frame' and comprises the total population of items (e.g. an area of woodland is the sampling frame, while the total number of trees it contains is the population).

Commercial or government polls and surveys mostly involve sampling: MORI for voting intentions at elections, Gallup for the Radio 1 weekly Top 40 singles chart. Even the Meteorological Office uses sampling: its daily weather reports are based on information from a limited number of ground observation sites in the UK (although satellite images and computer modelling are increasingly used as well). But don't feel that your data gathering has to be anywhere near the standard of these professional agencies.

Why take samples?

Sampling is an accepted 'short-cut' where there is simply not enough time, energy, money, equipment or labour force to measure and record every item in a population. It is easier, quicker and cheaper, making fieldwork feasible for the average student who has only 10–20 hours available for data collection, or less.

Remember that in most geography coursework you will be required to justify your sampling procedure, whether the theme is physical or human. Don't worry if your results are unexpected – as long as your sampling strategy and data collection are sound, this will give you additional scope for discussion in the conclusion to your report.

Photo: R. G. Jones.

Hints and tips 1: sample size

- Many coursework projects are fundamentally flawed because the sample size is simply too small, too biased, or based on one-off sampling. A sample which is too small is hardly worth having at all – no realistic conclusions can be drawn from it (you could end up proving that people with big feet tend to have big noses!). Around 30 is considered to be a statistically valid number of samples, but not if the whole population runs into many thousands (e.g. a sample of only 35 houses in a questionnaire survey about travel to work patterns in a town of 10 000 houses would yield an unacceptably low sampling percentage of 0.35%).

- Where the total population is less than 100, consider a complete sample (100%) or at least 50%.

- Where the whole population is large (and can be reasonably estimated) aim for a 10% sample if feasible (e.g. trees in a wood, farms in a rural area, shops in a city). The **Census** in the UK is partly based on this approach.

- If the population of your study area is unknown, e.g. barnacles on a beach, shoppers in a town centre, then don't worry about sampling percentages, simply adopt one of the methods described below, or use your common sense.

Hints and tips 2: groupwork

Groupwork is a real advantage, and often a necessity, when sampling. For example, when simultaneous sampling is needed - during traffic/pedestrian surveys at various points - or if the fieldwork technique requires more than one person – during river investigations and slope surveys.

Sampling in a group also means that more samples can be taken, thus increasing the validity of the results, and it improves personal safety and reduces risk.

Note: The new AS/A2 **specifications** allow for the group collection of primary data as long as your coursework carries clear evidence of individual aims/hypotheses, analysis and conclusions (see Appendix, page 103).

How to do it

The key to success is to decide on the sampling strategy (a design or plan of action) before you begin to collect your primary data. **Pilot surveys** are a great help in this process (see page 79), as are discussions with other members of your group, your parents and of course your teacher. Try the following approach – though it will not be appropriate for all fieldwork themes.

Step 1
Define the study area and **delimit** it on a base map (e.g. a town centre, a rural parish, a beach, a woodland, an upland area above 400m, a sub-catchment of a river (Figure 1). Note that some study areas are far easier to delimit than others. You may need to justify why you have defined your study area as you have. It may be appropriate to grid the study area, as in Figure 1, to allow easy reference and for the use of random numbers.

Step 2
Decide on your sampling strategy: point, line or area sampling on a random, systematic or stratified basis (see pages 76-78 for a full explanation of these approaches). This allows for **spatial** variation.

Step 3
Decide the sample size (or number of sampling points) and express this as a sampling percentage if possible (e.g. a blood donor weighing 10 stone will have roughly 10 pints of blood in their body so one pint donated equals a 10% sample).

Step 4
Decide if repeat sampling is needed at some or all of the survey points (e.g. vehicle counts at several different times of the day/week from the same location). This enables **temporal** variations to be noted.

Step 5
Decide on the support and equipment you will need. Learn how the equipment works (including its limitations) before you have to use it, and organise a pilot survey if appropriate.

Figure 1: Sampling points in the catchment area of a river.

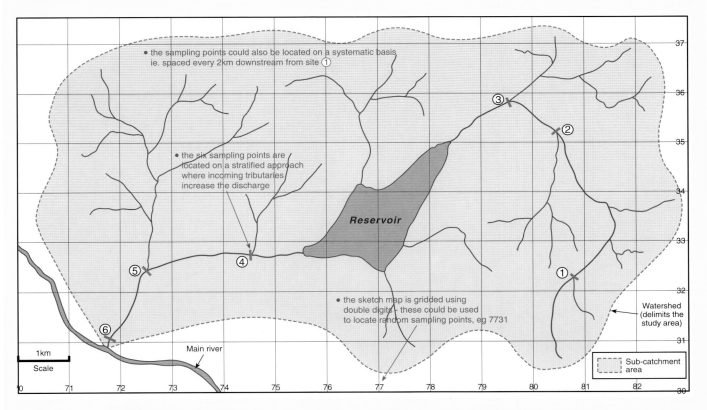

- the sampling points could also be located on a systematic basis ie. spaced every 2km downstream from site ①

- the six sampling points are located on a stratified approach where incoming tributaries increase the discharge

Reservoir

- the sketch map is gridded using double digits - these could be used to locate random sampling points, eg 7731

Watershed (delimits the study area)

Sub-catchment area

Main river

1km
Scale

Photo: Steve Day.

Sampling techniques

The first three options given here (random, systematic and stratified) involve point sampling, i.e. taking samples at obvious or suitable places (e.g. by a stream confluence, outside Marks & Spencer). In each case, the first thing you need to do is decide on how many sampling points you will need.

Note: Some coursework themes don't lend themselves to these approaches.

A. Random

This method avoids any subjectivity and bias in the choice of samples. It is best to use Random Number Tables (see Appendix), but you can also generate the numbers randomly using calculators, telephone books, dates of birth, etc. (or simply close your eyes and put dots onto a map – crude but quick). However, all random approaches can lead to unrepresentative samples if part of the study area is not 'hit' by the random numbers. In the example shown in Figures 2 and 3, a total of 36 random points have been plotted but only 24 of the 64 available grid squares have been 'hit'. The shaded zone represents the unsampled areas, and covers a significant proportion of the sampling frame (over 40%).

1. Overlay the map of the study area with grid lines, numbering them with double-digit numbers along the bottom and right-hand side.

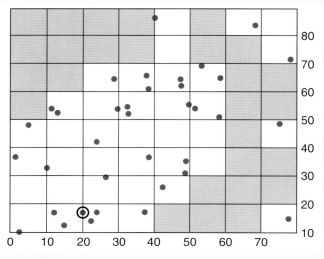

Figure 2: Random sampling points on a grid.

Note: If 'hits' fall on grid lines, as in Figure 2 they must be counted - you can allocate them to an adjacent grid square either to the right (for vertical grid hits) or above (for horizontal grid hits).

2. Locate your sampling points at the grid intersections of random numbers – in this example read 20 up the vertical grid line and 17 along the horizontal grid line (20 17 is the first pairing in Figure 3).

3. Note that some pairings cannot be used because they are outside the grid frame, e.g. 92 52 and 03 04.

4. Sample as close to these random points as is feasible in the field (you can't get into people's gardens).

5. Four-digit random numbers can also be related to distance along a 20/30m tape (e.g. 20 17 = 20m 17cm), or they could indicate survey positions along a hedgerow, a **transect** line, or in a taped area of woodland or sand dunes where quadrat sampling is undertaken. They can even be used for house numbers along a street (e.g. 20 17 would indicate a household questionnaire at numbers 20 and 17, or alternatively at house number 2, then the next one along, then the seventh one after that – the 0 does not count).

20	17	42	28	23	17	59	66	38	61	02	10	86	10	51	55	92	52
74	49	04	49	03	04	10	33	53	70	11	54	48	63	94	60	94	49
94	70	49	31	38	67	23	42	29	65	40	88	78	71	37	18	48	46
22	15	78	15	69	84	32	52	32	54	15	12	54	02	01	37	38	37
93	29	12	18	27	30	30	55	91	87	50	57	58	51	49	36	12	53

Figure 3: Extract from two-digit random number table.

B. Systematic

With this method, sampling points are evenly distributed or spaced in a regular fashion across the study area. If the area is gridded, then the sampling points (64 in this example) can either be at grid intersections or at the middle of each grid square (Figure 4). You then sample at the **feasibility** point closest to these points (e.g. the nearest house, tree, pavement space).

- Systematic sampling gives a healthy coverage and is simpler to apply than Random Number Tables. A grid does not have to be used - sampling can be to an agreed and uniform interval. For example, every tenth passing person in a street survey, every fifth house (or all the houses numbered '7' in each street), every twentieth pebble along a transect line on a beach, or every metre on a measuring tape along a hedgerow).

- These are all examples of systematic random sampling – you could just as well sample every fifteenth person that walks past you.

Figure 4: A grid showing systematic sampling.

C. Stratified

This method is preferred when the study area clearly includes *significantly* different parts or groups (known as sub-sets). The idea is to make sure that the number of samples or sampling points for each sub-set is fairly representative of their part within the whole frame. For example, for an infiltration-rate survey in a study area where three different rock types outcrop, i.e. clay, chalk and sandstone, if the chalk makes up 40% of the area and you have decided on 30 sampling points, then 12 of these should be based on the chalk sub-set.

In the example shown in Figure 1, using a stratified sampling approach 6 points have been identified where it is known that the discharge will increase significantly (mostly where tributary systems join the main channel). The stratified sampling method is not restricted to spatial zones, as in the above examples. In an attitude survey, for example, concerning a proposed Multi-Screen development, different age groups should be questioned in roughly the same proportions as they occur in the population as a whole. If the sample target size is 200, and elderly people make up 37% of the Census population, then 74 of them should be sampled. If people aged under 16 make up 18%, then 36 need to be questioned.

This approach is very useful in questionnaires where links or **correlations** can be made between sub-sets. For example, linking various demographic **factors** such as age group, gender, ethnicity, income level, or marital status, with information about the decisions people make and the views they hold.

**Retail core of CBD
= 30 sampling points**

**Park
= 10**

**Industrial
zone = 20**

Figure 5: Stratified sampling grid.

- You are conducting a pedestrian flow survey in and around a town centre. Your group has decided on 60 sampling points.

- You have worked out that the retail core of the CBD occupies 50% of the study area (or sampling frame), an industrial zone takes up 33%, and a large park takes up 17%. Thus, 30 samples should be taken in the retail zone, 20 in the industrial zone and 10 in the park.

- You need to allocate the sampling sites on a random or systematic basis within each land use zone (systematic in Figure 5).

Beware bias

In the context of sampling, bias is defined as a distortion in a statistical result; the result being very different from what is expected (e.g. bowls are weighted or biased on one side to bend them away from a straight or true pathway). Bias is inevitable in many geographical enquiries so your job is to be aware of this, to minimise its effects, and to discuss to what extent it has affected the validity of your enquiry (probably in the concluding section).

Examples of bias

1. A beach pebble survey where samples are chosen on the basis of subjective preferences (e.g. the roundest pebbles, or those which fit neatly into the palm of the hand).

2. A questionnaire survey of shoppers in a town centre where the people approached for questioning are only those who appear friendly and responsive (e.g. senior citizens, women with children). Note that the timing of shopper surveys can also result in a skewed or biased sample (e.g. if conducted around 10am on a weekday morning a survey will miss out most working people since few will be on the streets at that time).

3. An Environmental Quality Assessment of a predominantly terraced area of a town using such **criteria** as garden size, garaging facilities, satellite dishes, street furniture, etc., may well be unrepresentative of that town as a whole.

4. In making a survey of how well a class of students has understood something, teachers may question a few individuals only. The result may be biased (and so give the wrong impression) if those questioned are more able, or more involved, or more interested than the majority.

Photo: R. G. Jones.

D. Line sampling

Otherwise known as transects, lines used for sampling can be straight, angular or curved, and they can be drawn by connecting two or more random points. As a rule, existing routeways are used. Thus, for example, a road radiating out from the CBD to the suburbs might be used as the basis for an urban land use survey. In such a case, the **functions** of the buildings that front on to the pavement might be mapped or recorded, either continuously or at intervals of, say, 30m (Figure 6a).
Ideally, the line of transect should be orientated so that it crosses or samples as many different sub-sets as possible (a stratified approach). For example, in a sand dune system the transect could move through several seral stages from the shoreline and 'pioneer stage' to the 'climax community', with the middle of each stage being a sampling point. Depending on the context, a short transect line may be perfectly adequate (e.g. a distance of 30m up a beach from the **mean** tide level should allow a variety of pebble sizes to be measured on a random or systematic basis (Figure 6b)).

When undertaking vegetation surveys, belt transects with a width of 5-10m may be more appropriate in terms of revealing a representative picture of vegetation cover and **diversity** (e.g. a line transect may well not cross a tree or other typical species patch – see Figure 6c).

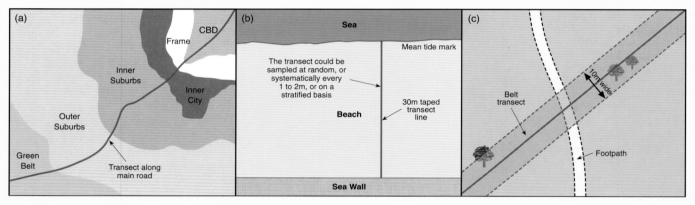

Figure 6: Varieties of line sampling: (a) land use transect, (b) pebble size transect on beach, and (c) belt transect of vegetation.

Comment on the sampling suitability of the three examples shown in Figure 7. Which is best and why?

Sub-set area

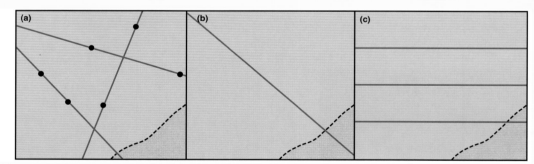

Figure 7: Three types of transects: (a) random, (b) stratified, and (c) systematic.

E. Area sampling

This is much the same as point sampling except that the squares are placed on the map or the actual ground and the occurrence of the feature you are studying is noted within the square. A quadrat is typically used in vegetation surveys to estimate percentage cover of various plant species (see page 95) and a similar technique can be used on beaches to estimate the relative surface cover of pebbles of different rock type.

Note on sampling techniques

In reality, it can be difficult to locate sampling points accurately using *any* of the above methods unless you have obvious ground reference points (e.g. a street plan, a stream system). For example, what do you do in a wood or an area of open moorland? Often, it is best to rely on local knowledge and/or common sense (e.g. take traffic counts at an obvious congested junction).

Pilot surveys

Defined as 'experimental undertakings or tests, usually in advance of larger scale surveys', pilot surveys should give a clear insight into the feasibility and timescale of your investigation, especially where equipment is involved. They need not take long to do, will certainly help with action planning and choosing sampling strategies, and if done carefully will save time in the long run (they may even demonstrate that your intended enquiry is not going to work!).

It is good practice to provide evidence in the data collection section of your report that you have undertaken a pilot survey. Give the date, time and location, describe the purpose of the pilot survey, and discuss what it taught you – and make sure that you incorporate these comments into the sampling strategy. It may well be possible to include the results of your pilot study within the main body of primary data that you will subsequently collect. Below are some examples of pilot surveys.

1. Questionnaires (see pages 64-67) Trial your proposed set of questions and directed responses on five to ten people, perhaps family or friends. Time how long each question-and-answer session takes. Identify suspect questions, consider if the question sequence could be improved and if the answers can be easily processed. It is a good idea to use an A3 presentation sheet with the pilot questionnaire on the left hand side and the improved version to the right. **Annotate** this with the reasons why you made changes.

2. Photographing (see pages 60-61) It is worth taking some sample snaps relating to your enquiry, especially if you are using a borrowed camera. This will familiarise you with the workings and limitations of the camera, and alert you to potential lighting or viewpoint problems. A classic mistake is to leave the film processing until it is too late to make best use of the prints, so doing a pilot will help you to work out the lead time you need.

3. Vegetation surveys (see pages 94-95) In this context, a pilot survey is important for giving you the overall feel of the study area and for identifying key species. It will also help you to decide on the best use of equipment such as quadrats or clinometers, and to work out the best places and methods for taking samples. Take a basic field guide with you for trees, plants, shrubs, fungi, birds, etc.

4. Risk assessment (see pages 68-69) A pilot survey to assess risk is essential in almost all cases. The main considerations should be your personal security (particularly in urban-based enquiries), and the impact you will make in the environment you will be working in. Remember, however, that a pilot cannot take account of everything, so think carefully about what additional risks might emerge later (e.g. much higher river discharge levels, being in London Docklands when Millwall lose a home football game).

And finally ...

If your data is largely **quantitative**, it may be appropriate to work out when sufficient samples have been taken, i.e. the required sample size (known as 'n'). First refer to the Hints and tips on page 74. In general, the larger the sample size the more likely it is to give a true representation of the whole population, but this will partly be dictated by the time and resources available. The steps shown below are based on a beach pebble survey:

1. Choose a transect line and collect a pilot or initial sample of 10 pebbles along this line. Measure their (a) or long axis in cm. Sort these lengths into **rank order**, i.e. 4.3, 5.1, 5.3, 6.4, 6.8, 7.0, 7.4, 8.9, 9.6, 11.2.

2. Using a calculator find the mean value ($\bar{x}$ = 7.2cm) and the standard deviation (σ = 2.0)

3. Decide on the tolerable margin of error you will allow either side of the pilot mean value – this is termed the 'confidence interval' (known as 'm'). For example, if m = 0.2cm, then you can reasonably expect the mean length of the full sample to vary between 7.0cm and 7.4cm. The smaller or narrower this confidence interval, the more rigour you are introducing into your sampling and the larger the full sample will have to be – so be careful.

4. Assume a 95% certainty or confidence level (the accepted level in most geographical enquiries). This means that you are at least 95% certain that the mean pebble length in your pilot sample will lie within the confidence interval of 0.2cm of the result you would obtain if you measured every pebble on the beach. Below this certainty level of 95% (or 19 times out of 20) it is assumed that chance will increasingly play too big a part. Convert the 95% certainty level by dividing by 200 (= 0.475) and refer to 'z' score tables, column A. This gives the value of 1.96.

5. Apply the equation:

$$n = \frac{(z\sigma)^2}{m}$$

So ... $n = \frac{(1.96 \times 2.0)^2}{0.2} = 76.8$

This indicates a required (or minimum) sample size of 77 pebbles. As 10 have already been measured in the pilot study, this leaves 67 more to collect.

Or you can continuously re-calculate the running or cumulative mean with each pebble you measure. When this value begins to stabilise without significant fluctuation then you have probably arrived at the required sample size.

'De-stressing statistics', *Geography Review*, vol. 11, no. 5, May 1998.

Soil Surveys

Although we eat fish (and even seaweed), we humans are mostly dependent on the soil – directly and indirectly – for our various sources of food. Soil is one of the key elements in the ecosystem, providing nutrients for plants as well as a medium for them to grow in: if soil is removed by catastrophic events (e.g. floods or high winds), it can result in dramatic losses of livelihood as well as wildlife habitats. Studies of soil are therefore highly relevant and can easily be linked to people and the environment in a range of interesting ways.

Limitations

- Soils lack street credibility, many students finding them dull, lifeless and irrelevant.
- Soil horizons in your soil pit may be indistinct. This is often the case with many UK soils.
- Soil studies often requires follow-up work in the lab using scientific equipment and techniques – not up everyone's street.

When to use

Because soils and vegetation are so closely linked, project work often focuses on the **relationships** between the two, for example:

- A study of the **spatial** variation in vegetation **distribution** and soil type.
- To what extent is tree height/girth/density controlled by soil type and depth?

Both these examples require soil surveys, as do studies which explore, for example:

- how soil **pH** changes from the top to the bottom of a slope or **catena**
- the influence of bedrock on soil characteristics, e.g. drainage, pH, texture, depth
- how soil texture, structure and chemistry is modified by the effect of different land uses and agriculture, e.g. ploughing, trampling, hedgerow and tree removal.

Before you start the survey

1. Decide what, if anything, you wish to link to your soil study, e.g. vegetation, land use, geology, slope, altitude.
2. Decide on how many soil samples need to be collected, from where and at what depth. This will be very dependent on your project aims and **hypotheses**, and how much time you can allocate to the survey.
3. Consult maps (Ordnance Survey, land use and geological) for ideas on suitable locations that are both accessible and safe.
4. Sort out all the equipment (and laboratory facilities) you will need well in advance of the data collection date.
5. Get permission from landowners to visit your chosen sites (and possibly dig a soil pit).

Photo: Steve Day.

Hints and tips

- It is often more convenient to collect soil with an auger (Figure 1) than by digging a soil pit. If you do dig a pit, remove the surface vegetation and put the dug soil on a plastic sheet. Ensure that you put everything back in place when you have removed your samples.
- Extraction and handling of soils must be the same at each site to ensure comparable results.
- Storage of soil is best done with labelled polythene bags (site or pit number,

horizon, date, etc.), secured with a zip tie (this reduces moisture loss). Samples should be analysed (at home/school) as soon as possible on return from the field site.

- Safety: at some locations there may be a small risk of toxicara – an eye disease spread by worms in dog faeces. Check with your teacher, family, etc., whether you need to wear plastic gloves. It is always a good idea to wash your hands before eating and on return home after working with soils.

Glynn, P. (1988) *Fieldwork Firsthand*. Crakehill Press, pages 32-34.

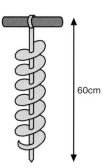

Figure 1: A soil auger.

60cm

Extension activities – 'lab work'

This should be carried out at school/college.

1. Water content: Put a small, weighed sample of soil into an oven-proof pot, dry for 2-4 hours at 100°C. Re-weigh and calculate the percentage moisture loss.

2. Organic content: Using oven-dried soil and a suitable container (e.g. a small baked bean tin) burn off the organic material (>600°C temperature is needed for about 30 minutes) and re-weigh. Calculate the percentage organic content.

$$\% \text{ moisture content} = \frac{(\text{raw weight} - \text{dry weight})}{\text{dry weight}} \times 100$$

$$\% \text{ organic content} = \frac{(\text{dry weight} - \text{burnt weight})}{\text{burnt weight}} \times 100$$

Soil survey techniques

Examination of soil horizons – depth and colour

The various processes which affect soils usually lead to the development of distinct layers or horizons. Soil scientists (Pedologists) give these layers different letters (Figure 2). Sometimes soil horizons are exposed (e.g. river cliffs, roadside cuttings) and can be studied easily. In other cases, either a hole must be dug to a depth of about 1m (which should be filled in after use) or an auger screwed into the soil (Figure 1). When this is taken out, the soil stays stuck to it, showing the different layers the auger passed through.

Horizons can be identified by differences in colour and texture. Usually they become increasingly stony with depth, and the top one is generally rich in **organic** matter. There are also likely to be changes in soil pH (see below).

- For each horizon measure the thickness with a ruler and record the colour. This can easily be done by 'smudging' the soil onto a piece of white paper and then cutting this out and sticking it onto your recording sheet (Figure 3).

Horizon	Depth (cm)	Colour	Texture	pH
L	3		-	4.5
F	2		-	4.5
H	7		-	4.5
A	34		sandy loam	5.0
B	20		clay coarse	5.0
Bg	12		clay	5.5

Figure 3: Part of a soil sample recording sheet.

Measuring the pH of the soil

By far the cheapest and most reliable method of measuring soil pH is to use a colorimetric method. This involves using either a pH kit (from a garden centre) or a 'BDH' soil test kit (which your school/college is likely to have). The essence of the method is that a colour change occurs in the soil indicator (similar to a universal indicator) when it is mixed with your soil sample. You then match the colour to a chart. Electronic probes are also available to measure soil pH but suffer from problems such as inaccuracy (although they give a precise reading), battery failure and poor **calibration**.

Equipment
- Spade
- Soil auger and sieves
- pH kit, soil thermometer
- Clear plastic ruler
- Sealable plastic bags
- Rubber or disposable gloves
- Recording sheets

UP TO ONE DAY

Estimating soil texture

Soil texture refers to the size of particles that make up the soil. Three categories are normally used: sand, silt and clay (loam is a mix of all three).

- The quickest and easiest way of judging texture is to take a small fistful of soil, wet it and feel it between thumb and forefinger. As a general rule, sand feels gritty, while silt is smoother and clay tends to be stickier.

- A **quantitative** technique is to sieve the sample using a stack of soil sieves of different mesh sizes (these should be available in most schools/colleges). Having dried the sample and removed debris such as stones and twigs, weigh the bulk sample before sieving. The coarser material (i.e. sand particles) will lodge in the top sieve pan, while the finer clay particles will sift through to the bottom one. Grades of silt and finer sand will remain in the intermediate pans. Finally, weigh each pan, expressing its contents as a percentage of the bulk sample. The results can then be plotted onto a triangular graph, with sand, silt and clay on the three axes.

Additional activities to think about:
- Draw a sketch map to note where samples are taken from, and possibly consider a short site description: flora, human activity, heights of trees, etc.

- Note down any evidence of waterlogging and of soil organisms (e.g. worms, centipedes). This may provide additional clues about soil structure and productivity.

- Measure the soil temperature with a thermometer. Sandy soils tend to heat up more easily and lose heat more quickly than clay soils.

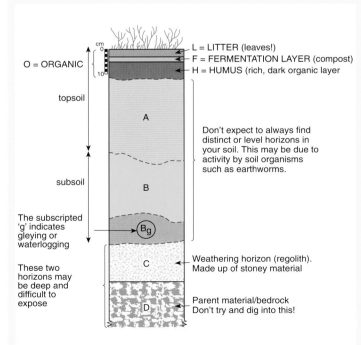

O = ORGANIC

cm
0

10

L = LITTER (leaves!)
F = FERMENTATION LAYER (compost)
H = HUMUS (rich, dark organic layer)

topsoil

A

Don't expect to always find distinct or level horizons in your soil. This may be due to activity by soil organisms such as earthworms.

subsoil

B

The subscripted 'g' indicates gleying or waterlogging

Bg

These two horizons may be deep and difficult to expose

C

Weathering horizon (regolith). Made up of stoney material

D

Parent material/bedrock Don't try and dig into this!

Figure 2: An example of a soil profile diagram for a typical UK woodland soil: Brown Earth.

'Biogeography: fieldwork approaches', *Geography Review*, vol. 10, no. 5, May 1997.

Transport Surveys

Transport networks are an integral part of the landscape and play a fundamental role in modern industrial, commercial, educational, recreational and tourist activities. Transport features are high on the current political agenda, particularly the need for local, regional and national integrated strategies involving pedestrians, cyclists, car-users, taxis, public transport and commercial vehicle operators (as well as airport and port services). Also, of much concern is the increasing congestion on motorways, in town centres, at major airports and on certain rail routes. The environmental costs of new developments such as bypasses and airport expansion schemes, and the problem of traffic-related pollution, are well known and pose a major challenge to policy makers. Given the wide range of topics and issues related to transport, there is no shortage of possibilities for coursework enquiries particularly at the local scale.

6. Impact and evaluation studies

1. Traffic flow counts

Transport surveys

5. Route quality

2. Journey generators

4. Car parking surveys

3. Public transport provision

Network analysis can be a useful supporting technique for some of the above surveys, e.g. **indexes** of connectivity, accessibility, detour/**sinuosity** and route density. (Refer to textbooks for further information.)

Limitations

- Even multiple sampling cannot reveal the complex nature of transport movements and patterns within a large built-up area. So your work can only be fragmentary.

- If you do not suggest appropriate solutions (on your own initiative or by researching policy statements) you will not fully deliver on your issues-based transport survey.

Traffic count or census

VERY SHORT BUT NEEDS REPEAT SAMPLING

This popular fieldwork exercise involves measuring the volume of passing traffic from a roadside or bridge position. Recordings can be made which focus on daily, weekly and possibly seasonal variations in traffic flow. This alone may provide the focus for a piece of investigative coursework.

1. Remember that you are a decision maker – ask the standard questions: *where, what, when, how* and *why?*

2. Choose a position for your count which is safe and gives you a clear viewpoint, but which does not obstruct the view for other road users, especially at junctions. Take care not to distract road users.

3. Sample for 15 or 30 minutes to gain a general impression. If working as a group, and/or surveying at a number of points, synchronise recording times. Be clear about the directions of flow that you are monitoring (one-way streets are easy).

4. Divide the road users into classes or categories, and record a tally as in Figure 1.

*Figure 1: Traffic **census** recording sheet*

Name .... Day/date ....
Survey site .... Map ref ....
Town .... Weather ....
Flow and direction (in/out or up/down or compass points) Time period ....

1. Bicycle = ¹/₂		2. Motorbike = ¹/₂		3. Private car = 1		4. Taxi = 1		5. Minibus/ van = 2		6. Bus/ coach = 3		7. Lorry = 3	
in	out	in	out	in	out	in	out	in	out	in	out	in	out
//	///	/	///	///// ///// ///// ///// ///// ///	///// ///// /// /	/		/////	////	//	//	////	//
= 2	=3	= 1	=3	= 28 = 14		= 1	= 0	= 5	= 4	= 2	= 2	= 4	= 2

pcu value (above column 4); *light commercial vehicles* (above column 5); *heavy commercial vehicles* (above column 7)

Comments: congestion; safety issues for pedestrians/road users; noise levels; car/bus occupancy rates; typical passing speeds (estimate only); on-street parking problems; impacts of traffic lights, filter lanes, crossing points and traffic calming measures; home base of lorries.

In the interests of personal safety, it is wise to have two people at each site, particularly on busy roads where both directions are being monitored (in which case, stand on opposite sides).

Further points to consider

- To allow comparative analysis, use the same survey site and time slot on different days. Then vary the time slot, e.g. peak flows = 7.30 to 9.00 am, 4.30 to 6.30pm, return school-run flows 3.00 to 4.00pm, low flows = 6.30pm to 7.30am.

- You may need additional people to do the following:

  a) estimate and record car and bus occupancy rates (Figure 2),

  b) note down the home base of lorries (which often appear on the sides or cab door– although this may not be where the vehicle has come from on the day of your survey),

  c) record the approximate speed of selected passing vehicles by using two fixed points (e.g. lamp-posts) which are about 200m apart. Convert the timing in seconds to kph and compare this to the speed limit. (If this is greatly exceeded, record the number plates and then ring the police!)

Score	Description	
1	Bus full or nearly full	At least four people in a car
3/4	Bus about three-quarters full	Three people in a car
1/2	Bus about half full	Driver and single passenger
1/4	Bus mostly empty	Just the car driver

Figure 2: Scores for occupancy rates of vehicles.

- Recording vehicle flows with accuracy may be near impossible on busy roads with continuously moving traffic. It helps to use a mechanical counter, or to group the vehicles into classes and allocate one to each person in your group.

- Roundabouts are excellent survey sites for recording the relative **distribution** of vehicles coming off a major road. Again, this favours a group-work approach. (Can you spot the deliberate mistake on this page?)

Photo: Paula Richardson.

In Figure 1, six lorries were recorded in a 15-minute period. Converted to one hour this = 24 lorries. Converted to pcu values (lorries = 3) = 72.

A step further...

Vehicle surveys can be converted to Passenger Car Units (pcus) per hour. Note that pcu values are not particularly realistic, i.e. coaches have a value of 3 (meaning that they take up roughly three times the space of cars) yet generally they carry far more than three times the average number of car occupants. Lorries have a similar value, but they carry goods instead of people, making comparisons difficult. An axle weight of up to 44 tonnes means that the stress they exert on the road surface greatly exceeds that of three cars.

With reference to Figure 1, add up all the class totals to give the overall pcu figure for the particular type of road that you are surveying. Compare this with Figure 3 and comment on your recorded vehicle volumes relative to the saturation level for that width category of road.

At saturation levels and beyond, the road cannot cope with the vehicle volumes, resulting in congestion, back-ups and even long stationary queues. There will also be frayed tempers, valuable loss of personal and commercial time and increased fuel consumption (leading to greater CO_2 emissions).

By using the observed occupancy figures for cars and buses, it is also possible to calculate the volume of people moved per hour past your survey point (it is difficult to estimate occupancy in a passing bus, but there may be a convenient bus-stop nearby where you can quickly check). Note: The passenger capacity of buses/coaches should appear in figures beside the entrance door.

Complete width (metres)	Typical road type	Saturation levels in pcu's per hour
4	Single lane road with passing places	<200
7	Two-lane country road, most 'B' roads and many town streets	375
10	Three-lane 'A' roads with central overtaking lane	700
14	Dual carriageways – many bypasses and trunk roads	1500
22	Six-lane motorways	3000
30	Eight-lane motorways	4000

Note: parking levels will influences these figures. i.e. a residential street, typically 7-8m wide will have a much lower saturation level if heavily parked on both sides.

Figure 3: Department of the Environment, Transport and Regions statistics for road types and saturation levels.

The pcu values may be useful evidence in discussions about the issues surrounding the use of private cars in busy town centres.

A further twist of environmental **significance** is to consider standard fuel consumption and CO_2 emission figures, as in Figure 4. Using this it is possible to calculate the overall CO_2 emission rate per hour at your survey points. This figure will vary depending on the vehicle type and volume, the efficiency of the vehicle engine, the type of fuel (diesel produces the most particulate matter, but is most efficient) and the vehicle speed.

Vehicle type	Fuel consumption (litres per kilometre)	Approximate CO_2 emission (grams per kilometre)
Motorbike	0.08	200
1000cc car	0.09	220
2000cc car	0.11	250
Van/minibus	0.12	300
Bus	0.40	1000
HGV lorry	0.55	1400

Notes:
- These figures are for average speed of 15kph which is typical for heavy urban traffic.
- 4.55 litres = 1 gallon (8 pints).
  1km = 5/8 mile (0.625 miles)

Figure 4: Standard fuel consumption and CO_2 emissions.

Vehicle type	Number per hour	Average speed (kph)	Approximate fuel usage (litres)	Approximate CO_2 emissions (kg)
Private car	1508	10	1400	3620
Bus	60	7	170	430
HGV	88	8	390	980

Notes:
- It creates a stronger impression when the vehicle volumes per hour are converted to ratios, i.e. buses : HGVs : private cars = 1 : 1.5 : 25
- This 'doorstep fieldwork' relates well to global environmental issues. It could lead on to a discussion about local sustainable transport policies within your town or rural area, and in particular the travel decisions made concerning the workplace, school/college, shops, etc. (see Journey generators opposite).

Figure 5: Sample street survey from Camden, North London.

Traffic trouble spot surveys

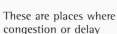

These are places where congestion or delay frequently occurs at 'pressure periods' during weekdays, and where individual vehicles are held up by at least one minute without necessarily being completely stationary, e.g. busy road junctions, approaches to roundabouts, road works, and particularly traffic lights (delay is easily definable here if waiting vehicles fail to get through a green light). It is when these are in close spatial proximity that serious delays can occur. Delays may also be caused by 'pulses' or 'bursts' of heavy traffic associated with, for example, league football matches and big local events, end-of-shift works' traffic, off-loading of large car ferries.

How to do it

1. Using a town street plan, mark on the direction of traffic flows and walk around at busy periods, mapping where delays occur.

2. In selective later surveys, try to quantify the delay by counting the average number of delayed vehicles, and the typical delay times, contrasting high and low peak conditions.

3. Try to account for these delays, suggesting a range of traffic management solutions (with their potential knock-on effects).

This survey could also be applied to rail networks. Delay times can easily be recorded at railway stations – the reason is normally announced. Rail operators (e.g. Virgin) generally display and publish weekly or monthly data on punctuality, delays and cancellations. Questionnaires can be used to explore this issue, but should not be used on railway property without written permission. A way round this is to tap into the student resource at your school or college. Some students/parents/teachers will be regular users of the rail network.

Traffic accident spots and traffic calming

All towns have their accident spots – local authority transport and police departments will have figures. You can observe, monitor and assess the degree of danger to road users, residents and pedestrians, particularly the very old and young. You can use risk assessment (pages 68-69) to score/assess potential hazards and dangers **qualitatively** – a good opportunity for problem identification and solution, and for researching in local newspapers.

Traffic calming measures include high visibility speed restriction signs, speed cameras, road surface colouring, rumble strips, chicanes, lane preferences, ramps and tables (Figure 6). From a safe roadside position, it may be possible to observe checks in speed, and, with experience, to estimate the passing speed of different categories of road user in the restricted zone. Such data could be used as part of a study of the relative effectiveness of different traffic management schemes (e.g. bypasses v traffic calming measures). The local authority should be able to supply facts and figures for calming measures and alternative solutions to traffic flow/speed problems.

Figure 6: Traffic calming measures. What is going wrong here?

Journey generators

As a result of increased mobility and choice, people now make longer journeys to shops, places of work, educational and leisure sites than was once the case. The 'pull' of certain sites, e.g. retail estates, leisure centres and large offices, generates heavy traffic flows which have observable patterns. These patterns, and the decisions that people take that affect them, make an interesting subject for study. You need to combine two approaches:

1. On-site surveys to appreciate the car passenger/pedestrian volumes and relative percentages involved (e.g. outside schools or colleges at the start and end of the day, at office/factory entrances, at supermarkets retail parks). You could extend this to consider the quality of the dropping-off, turning and parking provision, as well as accessibility to public transport. Related issues such as traffic congestion may also be relevant.

2. Questionnaire surveys: interesting comparisons can be made if the surveys are conducted in at least two contrasting (in **socio-economic** terms) residential areas or wards of a town. Each area should have at least 500 houses or units of accommodation. Aim for a 5-10% sample of each. Useful official data on population, car ownership and journey-to-work patterns is available in the Small Area Statistics held in the reference section of main libraries. The questionnaire should enquire about the range of decisions that influence particular journeys, as well as more obvious questions about the distances and frequencies involved, and the mode of transport used (see specimen question in Figure 7).

Figure 7: A specimen question from a journey questionnaire.

3. Which of the following **factors** most strongly influence your decision to travel to work by car? Tick the boxes that apply:
a) A convenient and secure parking space is generally available ☐
b) I enjoy driving and usually encounter little congestion or delay on the journey to work ☐
c) The car is essential most days for the type of work I do ☐
d) I have a car sharing arrangement with work colleagues which reduces the costs ☐
e) Public transport is not a viable option in terms of:
   1   Public transport stops are not close to my home/workplace ☐
   2   Unsuitable frequencies/timetables ☐
   3   Cost ☐
   4   Personal dislike ☐
   5   Crowded (may have to stand) ☐
f) I need the car to drop/collect children at school and/or for shopping/visits before/after work ☐
g) I enjoy the freedom a car gives me to listen to the radio/music, or to just think and relax ☐
h) I am not particularly concerned about my own contribution to air pollution ☐
i) I feel safer travelling in my own car ☐
j) Any other reason ....
k) I don't travel to work by car because..

Public transport surveys

Since bus deregulation in 1986 and the privatisation of the rail network in 1994, there have been significant changes in public transport provision which make interesting subjects for study. Bus or rail timetables provide the raw data needed for analysing the services and are generally free from stations and company offices. You can convert the daily/weekly frequencies into flow diagrams using a route map.

Try the following approaches:

• At bus/train stations, for selected routes and times, record the actual numbers of passengers getting on board (you can compare this with the capacity figure). It helps if a colleague can record the numbers of people getting off at or near the destination – this works well for park-and-ride schemes, where the occupancy rate of the service car park can also be monitored. Note that you will need to obtain prior permission to conduct user surveys at bus/rail stations where the land may be private property. Try also to record the category of passenger (age, gender, etc.), noting in particular those who may be dependent upon this form of travel (e.g. senior citizens).

• Travel the route yourself at different times to get a clearer picture of occupancy rates, the typical turnover of passengers at key stops, the passenger profile, and the overall service quality in terms of cost, reliability, frequency, comfort and convenience. Find out the fare structure, including concessions, and relate the charges to the distances travelled.

• Try to obtain secondary data on passenger usage from the operators (this is not always available). Other sources of information are local authorities (who release information on subsidy levels for certain bus routes) and rail companies (who hold season ticket data).

• It may be possible to compare the journey times of public transport between two points with car times, and to calculate the detour index (Figure 8). The less the time difference the stronger

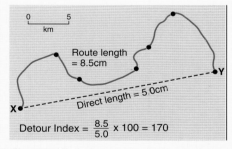

Figure 8: Worked example of a detour index.

the case for public transport, especially where **segregated** bus lanes and restricted access streets are in operation. The wider the time difference and the less passengers carried, the more unattractive and uneconomic the service will tend to be, although it may be a 'life-line' in some rural areas.

• Consider conducting a questionnaire survey of passengers regarding their reasons for using the service, and their thoughts on the quality of service provision. You can compare their responses with a non-using group such as private motorists (known as a **control group**).

Car parking surveys

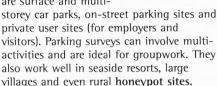

Of the various car-parking facilities in towns, the most common are surface and multi-storey car parks, on-street parking sites and private user sites (for employers and visitors). Parking surveys can involve multi-activities and are ideal for groupwork. They also work well in seaside resorts, large villages and even rural **honeypot sites**.

Location

1 First map the existing availability and distribution of car parking. If this covers a large area, split the study area into sectors and divide the survey job up within your group.
2 Produce a colour-coded/symbol map with separate keys for surface, multi-storey and railway station parks, parking meter/voucher sites, restricted sites (single yellow lines), private sites, free parking, casual sites (on unused land), illegal sites (double yellow lines, pedestrian zones, urban clearways, verge-side parking) and segregated parking spaces (lorries, coaches and disabled).
3 Find out the patrol range of traffic wardens since this will indicate a possible **sphere of influence** for car parking pressure.

Capacity

1 Find out the number of parking spaces available for both the local authority and private sector car parks (this figure should be available, but you can always walk round and count them yourself).
2 For on-street parking allow 6m per car if marked bays are not provided.

This should give you a rough idea of the total number of parking spaces available in your study area (i.e. saturation level).

Usage

1 Conduct a user survey at both high and low peak times to determine the occupancy rates of the car parks. It is possible that this may be close to, or beyond saturation levels at certain times of the day (i.e. overflow level).
2 Remember that car parking is a dynamic process – changes take place every minute, so your surveys can only be 'snapshots' at best.

Quality

Assess the quality of car parking, either for the whole town centre or, more feasibly, for selected car parks or streets. Consider the following **criteria**:

- Ease of access
- Ease of layout
- Cost
- Proximity to the town centre
- Concessions (i.e. long-stay, off-peak, seasonal, disabled, combination railway ticket)
- Capacity and the typical availability of vacant spaces
- On-site **amenities** (e.g. toilets, information boards/signs, litter bins, lifts)
- Safety/security for both driver and the car
- General environmental quality (e.g. graffiti, litter, landscaping)

You could devise a scale of 0-5 points to score the criteria, totalling to give an overall quality **index**. The higher this figure, the better the provision (e.g. a large, roomy and fairly easy-to-park site = 4, which may be short-stay and expensive = 0, but within the CBD core = 5).

Q: Comment on the planning issues that are highlighted in Figure 9.

Figure 9

Finally, discuss and try to evaluate the effectiveness of the parking provision and usage at both slack and peak times. Either arrange a brief interview with a member of the local authority transport department, or obtain the documented policy statements contained in the annual or five-yearly development plans. This may lead on to your own management plan which could involve changes in car parking and public transport provision, and even changes to traffic flows and routes in the town centre.

Route quality surveys

These can be applied to roads, public footpaths and even pavements.

Pavements survey

Pavements are vital transport routes for pedestrians. Start by mapping pavement width on a base map, indicating risk points and pelican/traffic light crossings. You can then assess the quality of selected stretches of pavement by using a mix of the following criteria:

- Width of the pavement relative to the pedestrian and traffic volumes (in a typical residential street 7m wide, each pavement should be about 1.75m = 25% of the road width).

- Surface type and condition, kerb height, quality of street lighting, animal waste and litter (chewing gum marks), weeds, degree of landscaping (particularly type and spacing of trees), obstacles (for disabled users, e.g. 'wheelie bins') and provision of litter bins and other street furniture (e.g. telephone/pillar box, benches).

Public footpaths

Particularly in rural environments, public footpaths can be assessed in terms of the following criteria:

- underfoot conditions, degree of maintenance (undergrowth, stiles, gates, footbridges), obstacles and hazards

- sign posting, **aesthetic** quality, plant and animal species **diversity**

- links with other footpaths (degree of connectivity)

For both pavement and footpath surveys devise your own scoring system, take photographs and conduct user surveys.

Impact and evaluation studies

UP TO ONE DAY

In relation to transport, enquiries of this type often focus on the impacts of either the closure/reduction or the expansion of routeways. Here are some examples:

1. The impact of a proposed or recently built motorway, bypass, ring road or link road.

2. The case for or against the closure or re-opening of a railway station.

3. Issues related to the expansion of an existing airport, either in runway or flight capacity terms.

4. Major changes in the traffic management of a town centre, including pedestrianisation and one-way streets.

5. The case for or against park-and-ride schemes, segregated bus lanes, cycle networks, etc.

For most of the above examples you will have to consider impacts upon:

- the local community and their quality of life

- the immediate built and physical environment

- existing traffic patterns, parking provision and pedestrian movements

- existing retail patterns

- the users themselves in terms of changes to journey times and journey quality

- other impacts (e.g. effects on habitats and animal activity, aesthetic quality)

Notes

- It is best to keep your survey to an achievable scale, concentrating, for example, on only parts of a routeway (e.g. the impact of a short stretch of a new bypass – only a few kilometres long).

- To study the impact of a new road scheme you need primary data on traffic flows prior to the development, or when the road scheme is still in the proposal stage. Local authorities should hold data for the former.

Example

A military air base has significantly increased its flight volumes in recent years. This has had an impact on the local area, providing the potential for geography coursework. A range of enquiry options are available, these include:

- Record the noise levels from a number of survey points using a subjective scale (see page 17) or a decibel meter. Monitor the prevailing wind direction since this influences the noise impact zone.

- Research the impact of flight expansion on local property prices and local employment. Conduct traffic surveys on access roads.

- Conduct a questionnaire survey of local residents and businesses to gauge their attitudes and feelings.

- From a vantage point (if possible) monitor the times, frequencies and flight paths of the air traffic. Record the data as flow lines and impact belts on a land use base map.

- Try to arrange an interview with the air base station commander/press officer (though they will not reveal anything of a sensitive military nature). You can also interview the local parish councillor or other elected person.

- Research the local newspapers for relevant articles.

Remember that military land is private property. Don't get yourselves arrested!

'Projects towards sustainability', *Geography Review*, vol. 8, no. 5, May 1995.

page 87

Urban Enquiries

Urban enquiries have always been popular coursework choices which, since over 70% of us live in urban environments, is not very surprising. As well as being accessible and familiar to most of us, urban areas have the advantage of plentiful supplies of secondary data which is easy to obtain (usually locally) and is sometimes free of charge. So, if you live in or close to an urban area, the range of urban investigations that you might undertake is limited more by your imagination and ability to come up with an appropriate aim/title/**hypothesis** than it is by opportunity. However, remember that good quality urban fieldwork relies on a mix of primary and secondary data; the better the balance, the better the end result.

How and when to use

A lot of what is considered to be urban fieldwork is covered in other sections of this book, as follows:

- Activity Surveys (pedestrian densities) (pages 14-15)
- Discovery Fieldwork (pages 30-31)
- Land Use Mapping (urban **transects**) (pages 48-49)
- Population Surveys (**Census** data) (pages 62-63)
- Transport Surveys (public transport, car parking, route quality, traffic counts, journey generators) (pages 82-87)

Your skill will be to draw the bits of this 'menu' together.

Towns and cities are continually changing and their present patterns result

from a mixture of evolution and planning. At present, for example, most towns and cities are in the process of changing as a

result of attempts by national and local governments to make them into 'places for people' rather than places for vehicles.

Historical change surveys

UP TO ONE DAY

You can investigate changes over time both in terms of the built-up area and in terms of changing population size and structure.

- Urban maps go back many centuries so they can be used to see which, if any, parts of the landscape remain. Often, relics from the past now form the basis for an important 'heritage industry', e.g. old warehouses along canals, historic buildings forming part of CBD conservation zones (converted to museums, visitor attractions, etc.). Progressive changes can be observed and analysed by studying and comparing maps in sequence (Figures 1a and 1b), backing this up with field observations of the current urban **morphology**. Depending on the scale of your chosen urban

environment, you can either look at the whole town or focus upon a particular area within it. (See pages 56-59 for guidance on using OS maps.)

- Interviews with long-term local residents can reveal a good deal about changes over time, as well as people's perceptions of those changes. Local museums and libraries are also invaluable sources of information, as are local history societies.

- Changes in population will have to be researched from historical Census data.

Try to link any population fluctuations to the changing fortunes of the town (e.g. development/closure of major industrial sites, war damage, major sporting and cultural events).

- A map could be drawn to show the major phases in the growth of the town (e.g. using the categories in Figure 3), with appropriate **annotations**.

Figure 1: Shrewsbury: (a) 1575, and (b) 1884. Source: Old Maps of Shrewsbury, FSC.

(a)

(b)

Mapping current land use

This will reveal any patterns that exist in the way that space is used in urban areas. It is best to focus on the CBD, which is the most diverse and easily defined urban zone, and to map the **functions** at street level only.

1. First prepare your base map. It must be **large-scale**, with the outlines of all premises shown (Goad town plans are good for this).

2. Divide up the study area into sectors of manageable size, bounded by main roads. (studying the sectors will involve group work.)

3. Decide upon a suitable land use key for identifying each set of premises. The seven generalised categories shown in Figure 2 can be used, but for a more comprehensive survey, use the specialised categories (in the Appendix). For example, an antique shop is categorised as B3a, i.e. B (for retail), 3 (for comparison shop), a (for antiques).

4. Working in pairs, map each sector placing the relevant coding inside each set of premises. If unsure, use a split coding. At your leisure shade the map and provide a colour key.

5. Comment on how the pattern of land use links to established models and theories (e.g. **PLVI**, core-frame model, **zones of discard and assimilation**, regeneration policies, pedestrianised zones).

Note: Street-level mapping excludes many offices, professional and personal services which tend to be found on the first and second floors where floor space is cheaper (e.g. solicitors, engravers, beauty salons).

Figure 2: An extract from an urban land use map.

A	Residential
B	Retail
C	Commercial/Professional
D	Industrial
E	Recreational
F	Public Buildings
G	Open Space
▨	Public walkways

Buildings: height, age, materials

A simple survey of these aspects of buildings is not enough in itself; you need to link one or more of the aspects to other patterns or issues. For example, linking building style (e.g. concrete high-rise blocks of the 1960s) to signs of social **deprivation** in the 1980s/1990s. In terms of patterns, terraced brick-built dwellings are typical of the inner city, while low-rise, glass and metal constructions are typical of science and business parks at the urban fringe.

- Building height can be assessed by counting the number of storeys (i.e. windows on top of each other) and assuming that one storey is roughly 3m high. Obviously, this measurement may be an under- or over-estimate, depending on the nature of the building, so you will need to adjust the figure to fit.

- To determine the age of a building, use the categories in Figure 3 and refer to the key to dating buildings in the Appendix (page 104). For example, many inner suburban semi-detached housing estates date from the inter-war period.

- Devise a classification system to cover the range of building materials used. The simplest grouping is: N=natural (sandstone, granite, limestone, timber, etc.) and M=manufactured (concrete, bricks, glass, metal, etc.), with additional letters to identify the particular material (e.g. Ns for natural sandstone).

Note: The design of the building shown in Figure 4 now looks out of place in a historic centre. It is scheduled for demolition due to concrete fatigue.

Category	Period	Era
1	Tudor	pre-1700
2	Georgian	1700s-1830s
3	Victorian	1837-1901
4	Edwardian	1902-1919
5	Inter-war	1920-1944
6	Post-war	1945-1970
7	Modern	post-1970s

Note: these are broad categories only.

Figure 3: Broad categories for estimating building ages.

Figure 4: Barker Street multi-storey car park, Shrewsbury.

'Make your own urban case study', *Geography Review*, vol. 12, no. 4, March 1999.

page **89**

Delimiting the CBD

UP TO ONE DAY

It is very hard to decide on where the central business district (CBD) starts and finishes in most towns, but there are clues. You need to think about the following as part of your coursework:

- Heights of buildings tend to increase towards the CBD. This model only fits certain large cities and some New Towns. Usually, the CBD of older towns/cities contains buildings of different heights, and the current patterns may reflect planning restrictions, etc.

- The PLVI marks the centre of the CBD, based upon where the main roads used to intersect. Since modern town-centre traffic management has largely re-routed these roads, PLVIs are now more flexible in their location (e.g.

pedestrianised zones, shopping malls). Banded rateable values are obtainable from Ratings Offices, but will take some time to collect and can be difficult to interpret.

- Land use mapping of commercial activities: Select some obvious 'blocks' within the CBD (i.e. blocks of premises, often bounded by roads). As a rule of thumb, where there is (on average) at least one shop in every two premises and one commercial premises in five, then you are in the CBD. A change in the character of land use may indicate that the CBD has given way to the 'frame' or inner-city (Figure 5) where individual uses take up large amounts of space (e.g. car showrooms, schools, large surface car parks).

- Pedestrian volumes (see page 14): These volumes decay with distance from the core CBD (Figure 5) so you may be able to use critical values to **delimit** the CBD.

- Traffic restrictions; there is great competition for space within the CBD, so mapping one-way streets, double-yellow lines, voucher/metered sites and the patrol zone of traffic wardens is one way of determining the extent of the CBD.

- Physical boundaries; these can make your job easy, e.g. rivers, inner ring-roads, parkland.

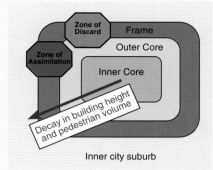

Figure 5: Modified core-frame model.

Residential surveys

UP TO TWO DAYS

There are numerous coursework opportunities for residential surveys, e.g. relating house type and density to suburban models or relating environmental quality to the **socio-economic** characteristics of an area.

a. Housing

This can be classified according to type, **tenure**, age and density (see Appendix for photographs), or by Council Tax band. There are eight such bands, lettered A-H, and the main **criteria** used for banding houses is their current market value, i.e. Band A represents the cheapest housing stock on the market, but this does not imply that it is undesirable (e.g. **gentrification** of Victorian terraces in inner London).

Type:
Terraced
Semi-detached
Detached
Bungalow
Tower block flats
Apartments in multi-occupancy buildings

Tenure:
Owner-occupier
Council housing
Private landlord
Housing/charity association
Sheltered housing

Age: Refer to Figure 3

Density:
Very high = tower-blocks
High = terraced streets
Medium = semi-detached/bungalows
Low = detached
Very low = country house/mansion/farm

Calculate the density by counting a typical number of units of accommodation in a **hectare**, using a large-scale Ordnance Survey map (the garden area should be included in this calculation), e.g. current greenfield developments are typically 20-30 units per hectare.

b. Environmental evaluation

This is notoriously subjective, with results often being influenced by, for example, the background, upbringing and perceptions of the surveyor. One way of eliminating these 'personal agendas' is to discuss the scores among members of a group; another is by calculating **mean** values from several individual assessments. Always try to assess an area from different viewpoints, including those of local residents – how would they feel if they saw your score values?

The unit on Judgement Surveys (pages 42-45) provides classification ideas, but it is best to devise your own criteria and scoring system to suit the area under study. When using environmental evaluations as the basis for comparing different residential areas, be careful not to base your conclusions on the crude totals of the

evaluations: remember that there are **factors** at play which may be beyond the control of the residents. For example, damage due to 'imported' vandalism, and reduced quality of life because of excessive noise, vibration and fumes from traffic.

c. Index of deprivation

The results of this exercise can be viewed alongside, or in combination with the results of other surveys, e.g. an environmental evaluation, to build up a fuller picture of the desirability of a particular residential area.

- An urban transect can be used to sample contrasting wards, or, within a single ward, you can contrast enumeration districts (EDs). From the Small Area Statistics (SAS) (see page 62), select a range of criteria which should give an insight into levels of income. In Figure 6, seven criteria have been used. Note that you will have to convert the raw data to percentages to make comparisons.

- For each criteria, allot rank 1 (highest) for the ward/ED which comes out worst (i.e. appears to be the most deprived) down to rank X for the ward/ED which comes out best.

- Total these rankings to give the **index** of deprivation (last column in Figure 6). The area with the lowest index would appear to be the most deprived and vice-versa.

'Deprivation and health in Sheffield, *Geography Review*, vol. 13, no. 2, May 1999.

page **90**

Figure 6: A sample of 5 wards in an urban district of 20.

Ward number	% males unemployed	% one-parent families	% households with more than 1 person per room	% households with no car	% households without central heating	% households with long-term illness	% head of household semi and unskilled	Total (Index of deprivation)
03BLAC	4	7	10	14	6	7	8	56
03BLAQ	1	3	5	7	4	2	4	26
03BLAY	11	14	13	15	5	12	14	84
03BLBC	8	16	12	8	16	16	11	87
03BLBF	17	12	18	13	14	10	18	102

Notes:
- From Figure 6, the conclusion can be drawn that ward 03BLAQ is the most deprived in this sample (but only based on these criteria).
- Although it is generally the pattern, don't always assume that high rankings = deprivation: for example householders may not choose to own a car for many reasons other than affordability, e.g. poor sight, or banned from driving.

d. Index of segregation

'Segregation' in this context refers to the natural tendency for people of similar age, occupation, religion or ethnicity to group or concentrate in close proximity (e.g. older people living in sheltered accommodation, students in flats/shared houses, Asian community in certain city areas). Look at variations within a ward, using comparative ED data. For each particular Census area use SAS (1991) to calculate segregation:

$$\frac{\text{Number of non-white households}}{\text{Total number households in ED}} \times 100$$

(In some urban areas the total may exceed 50%, in others it is zero.)

e. Residential desirability

- Produce a map of the main residential districts (delimited, named and numbered). Mark on obvious reference points (e.g. the town centre, main roads).
- Devise a scale of residential desirability or preference from 1-5 (Figure 7).
- Survey a number of people, stratifying your survey by age, gender, etc. Ask each person to score their own residential area, and to say which are the worst and best of the other residential areas (giving reasons for their decisions).
- Use SAS to reveal the socio-economic differences between the two areas (see index of deprivation).

Score	Description
1	A very undesirable residential location
2	An area you would rather not live in
3	An acceptable area to live in
4	A good area to live in
5	A most desirable residential area

Figure 7: Examples of perceptions of residential quality.

f. Hazard perception

An interesting approach is to produce a 'map of fear' based on people's perceptions of which places they see as 'risky'.

- On a map of your chosen study area identify places that you think might be risky both during the day, at twilight and at night.
- Use a scoring system similar to that for risk assessment (see pages 68-69), or devise your own. Ask a stratified sample of people to score the degree of risk for particular areas/streets from your base map. Also show them photographs of the same area at twilight and night and, again, note the score.

There may be clear differences in responses between males and females, between teenagers and older people, and between people of different cultural groups.

Industry enquiries

There are limitations as to what you can do in this field, partly because relevant data may be commercially sensitive and so unavailable to you, and also because of the limited range of data collection techniques open to you.

One possible topic is 'Industrial change over time', which could involve comparing heavy and light manufacturing industry in an area (see panels on 'Primary data' and 'Secondary data' for some ideas). Even for this study, however, you really need access to a contact in the companies involved, and preferably at a high level.

Don't forget industry comes in all sizes.

Secondary data
Company literature – old and new
Product lifecycle (sources of raw materials, where products are sold, etc.)
Changes in workforce over time, including structural changes
Changes in products over time
Profits/losses against production costs

Primary data
Site and situation map for company, including photographs
Large-scale plan of buildings, including process diagrams
Landscape evaluation, including air and/or water **pollution**
Interviews and questionnaires
Sphere of influence of both workers' residence and lorries to and from the works site

'Approaches to investigating the geography of crime', *Teaching Geography*, vol. 23, no. 1, January 1998.

page 91

Retailing and commerce surveys

a. Distribution of functions

- Start with a large-scale base map which shows individual retail/commercial premises (this includes vacant shops and land), such as chain stores, charity shops/'pound stretcher'-type shops, department stores, banks or building societies). Mark on the exact location of selected examples, and code with colours and numbers, as follows: if you are selecting banks, charity shops and shoe shops, use brown for banks, blue for charity shops and red for shoe shops, and give a number to each, for example, if there are twelve banks they are numbered from 1-12 (see worked example below) (Figures 8 and 9).

- Use a simple statistical technique (e.g. nearest neighbour analysis) to describe mathematically the **distribution** of these shops and services – clustered, random or regular (Figure 9). From the base map use a ruler to measure the straight-line distance from each numbered location to its Nearest Neighbour in centimetres. Then calculate the average distance between functions and work out the area of the CBD in square centimetres (see example in box). This technique is crude but may reveal certain **relationships** in terms of distribution patterns.

An R_n value of 0.36 indicates clustering of

$$R_n = 2\bar{d}\sqrt{\frac{n}{a}}$$

R_n = nearest neighbour value (must lie between 0 and +2.15)

n = number of services
a = area (cm^2)
$\bar{d}$ = average distance between functions (cm)

So,
$$R_n = 2 \times 0.9\sqrt{\frac{12}{300}}$$
$$R_n = 0.36$$

banks and building societies. This may be as a result of historical factors, or siting in an optimal location near the PLVI which carries status for this particular service. It should also coincide with a high pedestrian flow rate close to the PLVI.

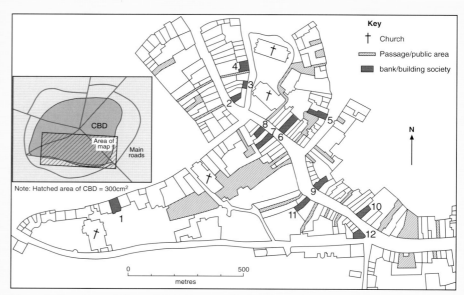

Figure 8: Carrying out Nearest Neighbour analysis for an urban area.

Note: The total area of the CBD (300cm^2 in this example) must be approximated by using the methods outlined on page 90.

Point	Nearest Neighbour	Distance (d in cm)
1	8	4.2
2	3	0.5
3	2	0.5
4	3	0.6
5	6	0.9
6	7	0.7
7	8	0.3
8	7	0.3
9	11	0.8
10	12	0.7
11	9	0.7
12	10	0.7
		10.9

average distance $(\bar{d})$ = 0.9

Figure 9: Tabulating data for Nearest Neighbour analysis.

b. Indicators of the 'health' of a town

These indicators include derelict space, vacant premises, and charity shops/'pound stretcher'-style shops. If the space occupied by such land uses is disproportionately large, then the area may be termed a zone of discard. You can take this a step further by introducing a **diversity** index.

Walk round the town centre and classify all of the types of shop/premises whilst tallying the total number of each (refer to the Urban Land Use Key in the Appendix, where there are 55 detailed categories - you can simplify this exercise by designing your own key). Then record and tally the functions from historical land use maps, such as a five-, ten- or 15-year old Goad map. Work out the total number of shops for each time period (N) and use the following formula to calculate diversity (DI):

$DI = 1 - \Sigma (X/N)^2$ where X = no. of shops of that particular category, e.g. food shops.

First work out X/N for each particular function, then add up all of the squared values to give a total for each time period. The diversity index ranges from 0-0.99, with a value nearer to 1 indicating greater diversity. Compare the DI values for each time period – higher values may indicate a healthier town. As an alterative to comparing changes over time in one centre, you could compare different town centres.

c. Footfall survey

Count the number of customers entering a particular shop(s) in relation to the number of passers-by (this is a two-person job). Compare results for different types of shop/premises, and see what patterns emerge if you link your findings to such things as business rates, shop frontage width, type of shopper, type of shop (e.g. comparison, convenience, department store, chain store), and whether any special promotions/offers are evident.

d. Shoppers' perception survey

This is to investigate shoppers' awareness of the layout of the CBD. You may be able to test the relationship between accessibility and land value.

- Select 5-10 named commercial uses of the CBD (e.g. shops, offices) (Figure 10), give each one a number and mark their locations on a map.

- Using a questionnaire, ask shoppers to match the numbers with the uses. Calculate the number of correct responses for each location (as a percentage).

Site no.	Function name	Percentage correct answers	Distance from PLVI (m)
1	McDonalds	73	80
2	D&P (pub)	37	400
3	Hawkshead	56	100
4	Marks & Spencer	84	60
5	Barclays Bank	63	20
6	Job centre	77	400
7	Tourist information centre	46	450
8	Ramna Curry House	14	550

Figure 10: Tabulation of data from shoppers' perception survey.

Note: High levels of shoppers' awareness or recognition could be explained by any of the following: popularity, location and obvious street presence. McDonalds is an example of all three.

e. Changes in retailing

People's 'shopping behaviour' has changed considerably over the last 30 years.

- Investigate how consumers feel about their preferred shopping environment (Figure 11).

- Plot the movement of people through a retail park or shopping centre and use footfall surveys to see whether food shops attract more people than other types (e.g. DIY stores). What other facilities, e.g. recycling centres, also attract shoppers?

- Using interviews with, for example, town planners, town centre managers, shopkeepers and Chamber of Commerce, find out in what ways your town centre is trying to maintain its attraction for shoppers (e.g. regeneration schemes).

Figure 11: An example questionnaire to test peoples' awareness of their preferred shopping environment.

We are sixth formers studying AS-level Geography at Sneed School. We are researching the changes in shopping behaviour in recent years. Could you spare a few minutes to help us to explore this issue by considering the following questions?

1 What is the name of the town centre/retail park where you typically go for most of your shopping needs? ....

2 What is your main **mode** of transport when visiting the above place? Tick the box
☐ Car ☐ Public transport ☐ Taxi ☐ Bicycle/motorbike ☐ On foot

3 What attracts you most to this shopping area? Please rank the most influential reasons by placing a (1) for the most important, etc.
a ☐ Close to home/work
b ☐ Accessible in terms of public transport (including frequency)
c ☐ Convenience of car parking (space availability, cost, proximity to shops, security)
d ☐ Quality and range of shops (including competitive pricing)
e ☐ All weather shopping under one roof, i.e. shopping centres, arcades and malls
f ☐ Personal security – you perceive it to be a low risk environment
g ☐ Facilities/**amenities**, e.g. clean toilets, play areas, provision for disabled, food outlets
h ☐ Pleasing environment for shopping (landscaping, music, displays, pedestrianised zone, etc.)
i Other ....

4 Is there any one particular shop or feature which stands out and draws in people like you?
☐ Yes ☐ No   If Yes, please state ....

5 Can you name two significant changes which have taken place in your chosen shopping area over the past 5-10 years?
a ....
b ....

6 What concerns you most about the present condition of your preferred shopping area? Please place an X against any that do not apply
a Crowding, particularly at weekends
b Difficulty of car parking
c Begging and busking
d Lack of suitable amenities (e.g. rest areas, shelter, lighting, toilets)
e Closure of shops leaving empty premises
f Growth of low cost shops affecting the overall image of the environment
g Groups of youths (male/female)
h Excess litter, noise and animal waste
i Safety in terms of traffic
j Lack of individual, family-owned shops
k Other ....

Is shopping a more pleasurable experience than it used to be? Please tick the appropriate column in the table below which reflects your feeling to each statement.

Statement	Strongly disagree (1)	Disagree (2)	Unsure/ don't know (3)	Agree (4)	Strongly agree (5)
1 Shopping areas are now more consumer-friendly					
2 Shopping represents better value for money than in the past					
3 There is now less stress in shopping					
4 Shopping can now be a leisure experience in itself					
5 Shopping areas are safer than they used to be					

Thank you for answering these questions and happy shopping.

Age: ☐ Teenager   ☐ 20-40 years   ☐ 41-retirement   ☐ Senior citizen
Gender: ☐ male ☐ female   Type: ....
(Obvious appearance, e.g. physically disabled, mother and children, ethnic minority, punk.)
Note: You should complete the bottom section discretely.

Vegetation Surveys

Wherever you go, in town or countryside, it is very difficult to escape vegetation. Plants and trees are solar-powered factories, processing air, water, solar energy and nutrients from the soil into vegetation growth. This in turn provides food and shelter for animals, and an organic windfall for the soil. There are plenty of small-scale **ecosystems** and habitats around you – woodland, moorland, wetland, hedgerows, river corridors, sea-shores, ponds, roadside verges, fields, gardens and parks as well as areas of waste ground, such as disused quarries. Given this variety of habitats and the issues that relate to them, there are many opportunities for interesting coursework projects, some of which might be linked to concepts such as environmental stewardship, **citizenship** and sustainable development.

What to survey

There are three broad areas for enquiry:

1. Vegetation species type, **diversity** and **dominancy**.

2. Percentage cover of vegetation (including bare ground), height, density and layering.

3. How the vegetation has changed over time (**succession**), how the species have adapted to the physical environment, and to what extent human activity has modified the habitat.

Limitations

- For non-specialists, identifying plants can be difficult, especially at times of year when flowers or fruits are absent.

- It is bad practice to remove wild flowers from the field site, even though this makes identification easier at school or home.

Woodland surveys

The following is a selection of the many things that can be done:

- Make a sketch map (to scale) of the study area (using an existing map as a basis if possible).

- Either compare/contrast several 30 x 30m survey sites within the same woodland, or compare/contrast two nearby woodlands (e.g. deciduous v coniferous) in terms of density, age, diversity, layering, ground flora, animals and birds, light intensity, etc.

- Identify and record the general **distribution** of the main tree species and stands, and comment upon the dominancy and density. Leaf/tree sketches and photographs are useful, and for help with species identification look

Hints and tips

- Many flowering plants and herbs die back during the autumn and winter months, so try to do your vegetation surveys in spring or summer (this may fit in well with the coursework). Use a simple field guide for identifying trees, shrubs and flowering plants.

- Plan your study so that **relationships** between vegetation and, for example,

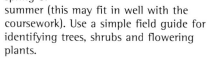

out for fruits, berries, flowers and nuts as well as leaves, etc.

- For selected trees, measure their girth (at waist height) and height (see Figure 10 page 21), and estimate their age (Figure 1).

- Measure the distance from each of the selected trees to its nearest neighbour and relate the height and girth of the tree to this measurement.

- Measure the light intensity (using a light meter) and see if there is a relationship between this and the species and age of the trees. Alternatively, estimate the percentage canopy cover using a quadrat held above your head.

- Record any evidence of woodland management (e.g. **thinning**, **brashing**, **coppicing**) and of woodland damage (e.g. by casual fires, bark damage due to deer).

climate, soil type, geology, altitude, **aspect** and air/water **pollution**, can be drawn out.

- Investigate secondary data relating to, for example, country parks, nature reserves, managed forests and sites of special scientific interest (**SSSI**).

Equipment

UP TO ONE DAY

- 30m tape measure, metre rules
- Light meter if appropriate
- Recording sheets
- Quadrats, trowel, sealable plastic bags
- Historical maps
- Camera/sketch pad

Species	Yearly increase in girth (cm)
Oak	1.9
Beech, Ash	2.5
Sycamore	2.75
Pine, Spruce	3.15

$$\text{Age} = \frac{\text{girth (cm)}}{\text{Increase in girth per year (cm)}}$$

Figure 1: **Mean** *increase in girth per year for different types of tree.*

Hedgerow surveys

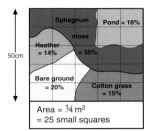

1. Select a 30m length of hedge and record its average height, depth and condition.

2. At intervals of 1-2m, record the vegetation found in the hedge. This can be done using a 0.5 x 0.5m quadrat (Figure 2) or by 'point sampling' with a vertical metre ruler, checking the hedge at 10cm intervals up the ruler. The quadrat results are recorded as percentage cover, but the point sample gives percentage frequency of occurrence (e.g. if ivy dominates at seven out of ten points, therefore ivy = 70%).

3. Record all birds and animals seen, and any evidence of their activity (e.g. feathers, droppings, burrows, nests, tracks).

4. Markedly different **microhabitats** and species may be found on either side of a hedge due to differences in aspect and/or land use (e.g. north/south, arable/grazing). Record and explain any differences you find.

Sampling with a quadrat

Quadrats are simple frames of two types. To sample the vegetation in a particular area, the quadrat is placed on the ground at random points. At each site, the numbers of different plants and the space they occupy within the quadrat (or each square of the quadrat) are recorded (Figure 2). Estimates of percentage cover are made for plants growing at all levels, from moss to tall flowers or grasses.

Sphagnum moss	Pond = 16%
Heather = 14%	= 35%
Bare ground = 20%	Cotton grass = 15%

50cm

Area = ¼ m²
= 25 small squares

Figure 2: Gridded quadrat.

5. Aspects of hedge microclimate can be measured (see pages 50-53). For example, wind speed recordings can be taken 1m above ground level on the windward and leeward sides of the hedge to measure the hedge's shelter effect. Differences in hedge density can be measured this way too.

6. In many parts of Britain, hedges have been replaced by fences or removed to create larger fields. Using historical maps and present-day visual evidence you may be able to trace (and map) some of these changes over time.

As the plants become smaller, more detail is required and so the survey area reduces, e.g. field flora = 0.25m² (Figure 3). Use quadrats at several sites to survey the field and ground layers, use measuring tapes (to create a sampling frame) for larger surveys, e.g. trees and shrubs.

Layer	Examples	Survey size (m)
Tree	oak, birch, ash	30 x 30
Shrub	bramble	5 x 5
Field	grasses, heather, flowering plants	0.5 x 0.5
Ground	mosses, lichens	0.25 x 0.25

Figure 3: Suggested survey size in relation to type of vegetation.

Note: In reality, plant species do not occur in neat patches so estimating is rarely easy or accurate.

Footpath surveys

These are generally used to investigate the recreational pressure on an area. The basic assumption is that different degrees of use of a footpath are reflected in the condition and type of vegetation both on and adjacent to the path. Surveys of this kind are somewhat overused in coursework so they need to be done well to get adequate credit from the marker.

Set up a tape measure **transect** line across the footpath, ensuring that both ends reach well into areas of vegetation that are undamaged (Figure 4). You can then measure the following (with repeat sampling):

- height and percentage cover of plants along the transect (note that some species, such as dandelions, can tolerate heavy trampling)

- infiltration or soil compaction (see page 39)

- path shape and deformation (measure path depth at intervals using a levelled line above the path)

Sketches and photographs are useful additions to a report, particularly if there is evidence of dramatic erosion, or of footpath management.

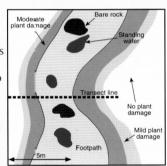

Figure 4: Footpath erosion survey.

Sand dune surveys

1. Set up a transect line running from the seaward side of the dune to the landward side (pioneer to climax). You need to survey obvious changes in the vegetation zones and in environmental **factors** such as slope, wind exposure, soil moisture, **pH** and salinity.

2. Use stratified sampling along the transect line, choosing points that are roughly in the middle of each distinctive vegetation or slope zone. At each site take a sample either using a quadrat or by laying out a 10 x 10m sampling frame using two tapes.

Within the frame, use random numbers to create co-ordinates which can then be used as sampling points (see page 106).

3. At specified sites, use a trowel to obtain soil samples. Bag, seal and label these. In many cases the soil texture and colour, pH, moisture and organic contents will have a direct influence on vegetation type, height, and species type (e.g. marram grass can survive in the low-productivity zone facing the sea).

The main findings from the above sampling

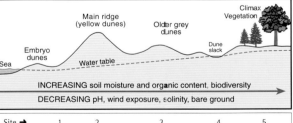

Site →	1	2	3	4	5
lyme grass	15%	-	-	-	-
marram grass	5%	45%	-	25%	-
fescue grass	-	5%	30%	15%	10%
heather	-	-	15%	25%	15%
pine trees	-	-	-	-	20%
bare ground	80%	50%	10%	5%	-

Figure 5: Recording sand dune information as cross-section and associated table.

strategy can be recorded as shown in Figure 5.

'Investigating coastal sand dunes', *Geography Review*, vol. 4, no. 2, November 1990.

page 95

Water Quality Surveys

The pollution of fresh water sources is an issue of grave concern in all parts of the world. When rivers, streams, lakes or groundwater become polluted the consequences can be far-reaching, leading to the disruption of complex **biogeochemical** cycles. For example, following an accident in a Swiss chemical factory in November 1987, the river Rhine became so badly polluted that birds, fish and **micro**-organisms were wiped out for 1200km downstream of the chemical plant. Also affected were cows, sheep and other grazing animals on riverside pastures. The sources of water pollution include animal waste and chemicals from farms, and human and industrial effluent of various kinds. Despite regulations to protect water from contamination, it still happens and you can find evidence for it from both secondary and primary sources.

Photo: John Reader.

What type of pollution to survey

Only some types of pollution are within the scope of AS/A2-level coursework investigations, and most of these are types of **organic pollution**, e.g. nitrate runoff from farmland. The complexities of collecting and analysing data for **inorganic pollution** (e.g. contamination of water by heavy metals) place it beyond the scope of most schools or colleges.

Most studies involve examining pollution from a point source (i.e. a single point of discharge). Examples include pollution of a river or stream by effluent originating from a factory, an industrial estate, a farm or a settlement (where there is a sewage outfall).

Safety matters

Apart from the obvious dangers of working near water, badly polluted rivers can cause serious risks to your health. Take precautions:

- Avoid direct contact with the water as much as possible, especially if you have any cuts on your hands. Wear protective plastic gloves and always wash your hands before eating both on site and on return from the field.

- There is a very remote possibility of catching Weil's (pronounced Vile's) disease which is spread by rats in water. Symptoms are 'flu-like about 7-10 days post infection. If you do feel unwell you should tell your doctor immediately that you have been working in water. It can then be easily treated.

- During hot weather, blooms of blue-green algae may appear as scum on the water surface. This will cause skin irritation. Again, wear gloves and remember to wash your hands.

Note: Most water courses in the UK are fairly clean and the risk of disease is very remote. If you are worried, contact your local Environment Agency Office for advice.

Limitations

- Unless you have access to expensive equipment (usually only available at universities), you can only investigate simple indicators of organic pollution, which is just one aspect of water pollution.

- Dispersed pollution is often difficult to measure or quantify as it is diluted by mixing.

- Aquatic fauna and flora are relatively slow to react to pollution. This means they are sometimes unreliable indicators, especially for episodic or short-lived pollution events.

How to do it

You should follow these steps:

Step 1: Decide on your aims and develop any hypotheses. You will need to select an appropriate sampling strategy, usually, 'above and below' or 'before and after' the outfall/source of pollution. How many sites will you have time to measure?

Step 2: Choose a stretch of river or other water course (e.g. canal). Consider map evidence, your local knowledge, newspaper reports and try to talk to people who live near to the river in question (for information about pollution incidents, etc.). The stretch must be of manageable size for the scale of your study.

Step 3: Determine what characteristics of the river you will investigate. The potential techniques fall into two categories:

- Environmental (shaded green): (1) **indicator species** (animals and plants), (2) visual evidence (smell, flotsam/litter, and effluent discolouration), (3) temperature (calefaction) and flow circulation, and (4) **turbidity**.

- Chemical (shaded purple): (1) dissolved oxygen, (2) nitrates and pH.

(You will need to refer to other books/ sources for information on other techniques. Check out the references at the bottom of these pages.)

Step 4: Contact the Environment Agency (see page 111) for any secondary data on your chosen stretch of water. You will have to be very clear and specific about your needs.

Equipment

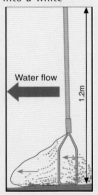

UP TO HALF A DAY

- Kick net, tray, indicator key
- Secchi disc
- Nitrate strips, O_2 probe, thermometer
- Sample bottles, **pH** kit
- Plastic (disposable) gloves
- Disinfectant for heavily polluted areas
- Recording sheets

1. Animals and plants as indicators

If a fresh water body is 'healthy', you can generally expect to find a wide variety of plant and animal species living in/on the water. The types, numbers and **distribution** of these indicator species (e.g. Figure 1) can be used to gauge the quality of the water. There is usually a progressive loss of clean water animals the closer you get to the source of pollution, and the presence of certain plants is an indication of pollution (e.g. sewage fungus, blanket weed).

Figure 1: Mayfly as a high O_2 demander is an indicator of clean water.

Sampling invertebrates: You need a net with fine mesh (about 0.1mm) and preferably a flat base (Figure 2). Use a 'kick sampling' method, i.e. catch the organisms by kicking the stream bed and dislodging stones (kick upstream of your net and the animals will be washed into the net). Kick for the same amount of time at each of several sites – say 30 seconds. Empty the net into a white sampling tray and sort the animals according to type (see Appendix, page 107). You can then classify and count the animals according to their tolerance of pollution and demand for oxygen – identification is best done on site. You must carefully return the animals to the stream afterwards.

Water flow

1.2m

Figure 2: Kick sampling net.

2. Visual evidence

You will need to design and prepare a suitable sheet to record your **qualitative** observations, for example, of smell, effluent discolouration, rubbish.

3. Temperature and flow rate/circulation

Temperature is important in controlling stream oxygen levels. To measure it, use a thermometer/probe, and to measure flow rates use a flowmeter or float (see pages 25-26 for details).

4. Turbidity

The main reason for water being turbid, or opaque, is because it contains suspended sediment; however, it can also be a sign of pollution. To assess turbidity, you can use either a Secchi disc (Figure 3) or a square painted tile. The disc/tile is lowered into the water on a string at various sites, and the depth at which it can no longer be seen is recorded. Compare the findings for different sites.

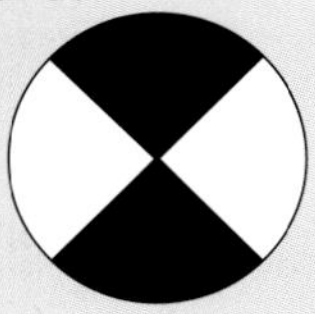

Figure 3: Secchi disc.

1. Dissolved oxygen

Oxygen is essential for life in streams and rivers, and is used by bacteria during the decomposition of organic remains. This means rivers with low oxygen concentrations may be suffering from pollution by, for example, raw sewage, effluent from paper mills or food processing plants, agricultural waste or products (in particular, silage). Measurement of oxygen concentrations is best done with a meter or oxygen probe, so check first to see if your school/ college has one you can use (Phillip Harris supplies these – see page 111). The colder and faster flowing a river, the greater its capacity to exchange oxygen with the air, and the cleaner it should be.

2. Nitrates and pH

Nitrates are essential for plant growth, but levels of 50 **ppm** are the recognised limits for potable (safe to drink) water. Nitrates in water come from either the soil (perhaps through agricultural pollution) or from sewage, and are associated with **eutrophication**. The simplest and cheapest method of detection is to use test strips and a 'Nitrachek' meter available from Merck (see page 111). Alternatively, cheap kits for testing selected chemicals can be bought in most garden centres, but they are not very reliable. The tests can be carried out in the field or on a sample immediately after you return to base.

To measure pH, use a simple probe or chemical testing kit (which your school/ college will probably have).

Other measures

- The Department of the Environment, Transport and the Regions (DETR) classifies river pollution on a scale of 1-4 based on the types of organisms present (see references below).

- The Trent Biotic Index (designed for non-scientists to assess water pollution) involves giving **quantitative** scores of between 0-15 (see references below).

Williams, G. (1987) *Techniques and Fieldwork in Ecology*. Collins Educational, pages 96-100.

X-Files

Be warned – you are now entering a classified zone! The aim here is to alert you to some of the major offences that you might commit, or come close to committing, when you do your coursework. Some of the examples given may seem far-fetched, but they are all taken from real cases. So, to avoid the pitfalls, enter here *before* you start on your coursework, and get out quickly before you are overcome with despair ...

How to use

Each X-file has been scored on a 'danger scale' from 1-10 – not everyone would agree with the authors' decisions, but it is a useful guide. The higher the score the more serious the mistake, so something that scores 1 is harmless, and that scores 2 is unlikely to lead to any loss of mark, but anything that scores from 3 upwards is likely to create a poor impression, or worse.

Lethal X-files

Don't come near these. They are likely to go off in your face.

Score	X-file
10	**Fraud crime:** You more or less copy another student's coursework, including the presentation techniques, analysis and conclusions, or you even download a complete project package (this has been done!)
10	**Stupidity crime:** You lose the coursework and have no back-up copy. Definitely not smart.
9	**Organisation crime:** Your report is hopelessly disorganised with no clear sections or cross-references and no logical enquiry route. A dog could have put it together better.
8-9	**Selection offence:** The enquiry site for your project is too remote, or the project is too large in scale. There will be obvious problems of transport, safety, accommodation, funds, secondary information. Family holiday destinations are often disastrous fieldwork opportunities. Just stick to enjoying yourself instead.
8	**Sampling offence:** This is one of the most common – reports are entirely over-dependent on highly suspect and limited sampling techniques such as questionnaires and quadrat surveys. Sweeping conclusions are drawn from the flimsiest of evidence (e.g. only 10 questionnaires, or a few hopeful quadrats). Does this ring a bell?

Critical X-files

If you hit these you are either wasting a serious amount of your own time, or have more or less ignored advice from teachers, or you have lost the original plot. Watch out!

Score	X-file
7	**Boredom offence:** You have not the remotest interest in your coursework. It soon becomes your worst enemy and this shows when you finally come to hand in the report.
7	**Non-geographical crime:** Your coursework becomes separated from the geographical aspects of the investigation (e.g. the study of an urban conservation zone becomes bogged down in long and tedious descriptions of architecture, historical change, ownership, planning procedures).
6	**Deadline offence:** You leave the writing up of your coursework too close to the delivery deadline, giving you personal grief and anxiety, and affecting those you live with. Students have been known to stay up for several all-night sessions to complete their coursework. Quality obviously suffers. Try action-planning and keeping to schedules.
6	**Plagiarism crime:** You spend hours copying out paragraphs and even whole pages from books, articles or brochures and you do not even acknowledge or reference them. This **plagiarism** (or 'lifting') crime may carry serious consequences. Read the awarding body **specifications** to see what the penalty might be.

Serious X-files

This is a more widespread category of coursework blunders. Try to avoid them.

Score	X-file
5-6	**Ignorance offence:** You disregard the official mark scheme, particularly the **weightings** for each section. Many students write far fewer than 300 words for the evaluation and conclusion section, which is often worth up to 25% of the total marks. Others go overboard when describing the various methodologies for data collection, which may only be worth 15% (see Introduction, page 5).
5	**Photo offence:** Your project turns into a glorified photograph album. It is neatly organised and may look good, but lacks proper selection, integration and analysis.
5	**Writing offence:** You overlook the fact that your study report is an exercise in communication skills: spellings are not checked, punctuation and grammar are poor, there are too many long passages that need breaking down into crisp paragraphs, some sentences are far too long and you seldom use the best terminology for the job.
5	**Graphs offence:** You include too many (often repetitive) computer generated graphs simply because they look nice and fill out the report. The current world record is 223 pie charts in a single project!
4-5	**Map crime:** You supply a barely improved photocopied base map to show the study area, without your personal 'stamp' of improvement on it. Include **annotations**, key, scale, etc.

Intermediate X-files
These are less serious crimes but watch out as an accumulation of them may damage your health.

Score	X-file
4-5	**Incompetent group offence:** Your group is dysfunctional – you don't get on with each other that well, some members are unreliable, and there is little worthwhile discussion. Roles and jobs may not be well defined or appropriate to the tasks involved and the skills are not complementary (e.g. nobody knows how to use random number tables, draw up a spreadsheet or design a worthwhile questionnaire).

4+   **Coursework re-hash crime:** You decide to re-do an old piece of coursework (e.g. your GCSE project) with a few minor embellishments. Depending on how good it is in the first place, this could be dangerous and get a worse score than 4.

4   **Hypothesis offence:** The study is loaded with too many **hypotheses**, some of which may overlap with each other, are too obvious or are not relevant to the aim of the study. Try to restrict yourself to a single narrow focus, e.g. a group of students is asked to investigate how and why pedestrian flows vary in their town centre. The group collects primary data and from this a number of succinct individual hypotheses can be followed up. Is there a significant **relationship** between the location of major car parks and high pedestrian flow values?.

4   **Simplistic offence:** Your report is too simplistic, it is based on a hypothesis, question or idea which is self-evident (too obvious), e.g. river discharge increases downstream or traffic congestion is most severe during rush hour.

3-4   **Planning offence:** Beware of project titles to do with planning issues. This may be OK if you actually intend to participate in the planning process and if there is ample secondary information available, otherwise this could be dangerous ground. Talk to and interview planners, supporters, objectors, etc.

The lesser X-files
These are the least serious offences. But cut them out and you can deliver a classy piece of work.

Score	X-file
3-4	**Word-limit crime:** You clearly over-run the official word limit, demonstrating a lack of planning and review skills, and an inability to keep to the 'spirit' of the exercise.
3	**Introduction offence:** Your introduction fails to be snappy, relevant and interesting. It is too long, poorly focused, tedious and sends people to sleep.
3	**Numbering offence:** You forget to number your diagrams in sequence, or to use page numbers – a minor but often costly mistake which spoils the flow of your report and makes referencing difficult.
3	**Equipment crime:** Examples include forgetting to locate and book equipment in time, failing to liaise with other users, not learning how to use it or what to do if it breaks down.

2   **Confetti crime:** When shaken, items fall out of your finished report like confetti (and what if there are no page numbers?)

2   **Plastic wallet crime:** Avoid including too many plastic A4 wallets, and make sure the contents are visible (if not, they may not be looked at). Label the wallets and state what each map shows. Avoid stapling A3 maps or diagrams so that they cannot be opened.

1-2   **IT offence:** Your only use of information and communications technology is to word-process the report and to generate a few graphics/charts. Why not make use of the Internet and CD-ROMs to give wider significance and a social/political dimension to your study?

1   **Key Skills crime:** You fail to 'signpost' your key skills. A good piece of coursework could so easily be a portfolio of evidence, demonstrating your skill achievement in problem solving, working with others and processing numerical information, etc.

And finally

Choose a project title or theme which suits your ability level. Consider taking a **skills audit** – try and score yourself on a scale of 0-5. If you are academically strong then go for projects which give you the opportunity to explore the wider political, social, economic and environmental **significance** of your report, which can be drawn out in your conclusion. Alternatively, take good advice and make your project achievable within your own personal limitations. It is all about horses for courses.

Subject knowledge	
Artistic and **aesthetic** skills	
Empathy skills	
Numeracy and IT skills	
Communication skills	
Working with others	
Evaluation and analytical skills	
Practical skills	
Total	

Time to score

Once your coursework is complete, try using the X-files to score it according to the overall danger scale. Anything over 10 should concern you, over 20 and you are sailing through dangerous waters, over 30 and you are sunk without trace. Have you ever considered a free transfer to another subject?

This is classified information – there are no references other than those in the vaults of MI5.

Yawn Projects

Like most new products and initiatives, geographical coursework needs a periodic 'new look' to maintain its appeal. It is inevitable that fieldwork should have lost some of the appeal of the early days – for students, staff and Examiners alike. Now, especially given the pressures from other subject areas, the prospect of fieldwork can be daunting or even boring. Also, many of the 'best' themes have been done too often, resulting in **'fieldwork fatigue'** among Examiners as well as staff. All is not lost, however – especially if you read this unit and the list of Suggested Project Titles on pages 10-13 of this book. With luck, these will encourage you to tackle new and interesting ideas – and to avoid some pitfalls (see also the X–Files unit).

Anti-yawn strategies

1. Stick to a predictable and popular theme or idea but think of ways in which you can inject something individual, lively and thoughtful which will lift it out of the well-worn ruts.

2. Collect data as a group exercise and then 'spin-off' into your own more focused enquiry. An example of this is in Rural Enquiries (pages 70-73), where a dozen or more potential titles can be generated from an umbrella approach.

3. If your course allows it, take the optional written practical examination, although this will require some fieldwork skills and possibly a short fieldwork report.

4. Check out the three worked examples below. In each case a well-worked theme has been developed in such a way that the project is achievable and manageable, and, we hope, interesting and challenging.

5. Give up geography – a fairly drastic and ill-advised course of action.

Example 1: 'What will be the effects of the new bypass on town X?'

The main problems with a title like this are:
- the scale of the enquiry may be too large;
- the term 'effects' is broad and vague;
- it is necessary to know something about what it was like before the bypass was constructed (e.g. traffic flows, parking, accidents, crossing points, noise, fume and vibration levels), and few students do the necessary research;
- it often takes several years for traffic fully to utilise new road systems;
- if the bypass is only at the proposal stage, or under construction, then the potential impacts are largely a matter of guesswork.

So why not change the title to:

1 'The case for or against the proposed/ actual bypass.'

2 'An environmental impact assessment of two optional bypass routes.'

3 What percentage of the traffic has transferred from the old main road through settlement X to the new bypass, and what have been the main consequences of this?'

4 'What do the residents and trades people feel about the traffic issue in X?'

5 'An evaluation of the traffic calming measures in Y.'

6 'An analysis of the congestion and hazard sites along the main road in Z.'

7 'During peak times of the day, traffic reaches saturation levels along the main road in Q.'

8 'Should HGVs be banned from passing through the village of R?'

Choosing a sensible and achievable title for your project does not guarantee success, however. As with many human geography themes you must be prepared to research official documentation, to conduct **pilot surveys** and to resist the temptation to become reliant on sub-standard questionnaires.

Note: Some of the alternative titles given here offer scope for reaching an informed decision, and possibly for putting forward a management plan. This is the very essence of effective coursework.

Figure 1: Shrewsbury A5 bypass.

Example 2: 'An investigation into the impact of tourism upon settlement/site X'

This example has been done to death, but that doesn't mean that it cannot be developed into a meaningful and successful piece of coursework.

The main problems with this title are:

- deciding on who the tourists are (how do you recognise them?);
- the term 'impact' is vague and over-used in geography and it can lead to inconclusive projects which have as much substance as a jelly;
- it often results in sweeping conclusions based on one-off site visits, and exaggerations about the scale of certain problems (e.g. 'tourists create mountains of litter');
- the term 'impact' is often perceived in a negative way only (e.g. tourists damage footpaths, cause congestion);
- **temporal** variations are seldom considered (e.g. tourist/visitor pressure off-season), as are **spatial** variations (i.e. between sites).

So, why not change the title to:

1 'Are the facilities and **amenities** at X sufficient to meet the needs of visitors?'

Figure 2: The car park at Lulworth Cove, Dorset in 1974.

2 'The more popular a **honeypot site**, the more extensive its **sphere of influence**'

3 'Is the Countryside Park at Y an under-used resource?'

4 'What evidence is there that tourists have a strong seasonal effect on town/resort Z?'

5 'Is there a clear difference between visitors and residents in terms of their perception of a holiday resort?'

6 'A survey of tourism at site R in terms of visitor type and numbers, duration of stay, activities and issues.'

7 'There is a distance-decay effect from the car park at site N in terms of visitor numbers, noise and litter.'

You will notice that these alternative titles have a narrower and clearer focus. The second and last are hypotheses, and as such provide a framework for achievement (possibly allowing the application of statistical techniques).

Example 3: 'An enquiry into the retail changes in the CBD of town X'

The main problems with this title are:

- no time period has been suggested;
- depending on the size of the town, the project may become unmanageable;
- it may be difficult to **delimit** the CBD effectively (many students fail to do this);
- it is easy to overlook the influence of **factors** beyond the CBD (e.g. edge-of-town retail parks, the national economy, changes in consumer demand and fashion, increased mobility and choice). In other words, students fail to give the enquiry a wider **significance**.

So, why not change the title to:

1 'Is there a more rapid turnover of shops in town centres now than in the past, and what factors have influenced this?'

2 'What is the percentage of charity shops and vacant premises in the town centre of X and do these indicate commercial ill-health?'

3 'What factors account for the sluggish build-up of custom on most Saturday mornings in town Y?'

4 'Is there a new breed of retail **functions** which did not exist in town centres up to 20 years ago? If so, what are the reasons for this and is there any pattern to their location?'

5 'What evidence exists that area Y of the CBD is becoming run-down and may be a **zone of discard**?'

And finally

Some dodgy titles to avoid, if you can resist the temptation.

- 'The impact of new shopping centres upon retail patterns in town X' (most data will be confidential).
- 'An evaluation of the retail park/industrial estate at Y' (too vague).
- 'An assessment of the quality of life in two contrasting urban wards' (over-reliant on **Census** data).
- 'The impact of agricultural/industrial operations on the river N' (seldom achievable).
- 'Traffic problems in M' (absurdly brief).

Zero Tolerance

Now that we have got this far, the authors would like to admit that they have clean run out of steam. And they could not think of a technique, trick or tactic beginning with Z – except for Zoo Surveys, which didn't do much for them. But life is a zoo of sorts, including your school or college. So here is a final reminder that your teachers and student colleagues are a varied species indeed. Their attitudes, values, fears, perceptions and personal decisions may well provide valuable ammunition for your geography coursework. They might be a rich seam of primary data – so why not try being a miner, and start digging for a few days.

And as for Tolerance – this is defined as:

> 'Allowing and accepting the existence of other people's opinions, values and acts, particularly where they may differ from your own'.

Geography as a subject gives you the opportunity to explore this quality, and through coursework to take it a stage further and demonstrate it. Tolerance also extends to various physical environments you will be working in. The whole idea of fieldwork is to make you a more observant and questioning student, and to promote your understanding and awareness of the world around you. Fieldwork becomes counter-productive if you leave places in a worse state than you found them, or if the whole exercise becomes no more than a mechanical data-gathering activity. Take stock of your surroundings and try to appreciate some of their mystery and complexity – it doesn't cost you a penny and you have everything to gain.

That's it – apart from a few personal comments to see you on your way. Don't forget to refer to the pages at the end of this book, as and when you need them.

Take good care of yourselves and watch your backs out there.

Now get this. I hope this effort hasn't been a total waste of time. But then my life has been full of doubts, misgivings and mistakes. Just like your geography coursework? After all, nobody said that life was going to be easy.

Dave Farbrother – co-author

Hear me out. Unlike the other author, I can actually remember doing geography at school. I also recollect the struggle of coursework and its delivery. No matter what you read, in whatever book or article, nothing can really prepare you for this event. Read the guidelines, get as much help from teachers and family and friends as you possibly can, and above all, stay cool.

Dave Holmes – co-author

I've written more books than some of you have had hot dinners – so listen to this. Fieldwork gives you the freedom to do what you want, to plan and organise an enquiry on a matter that interests or concerns you, in an environment that may possibly stimulate you. So there!

Sue Warn (Chief Examiner, Edexcel)

Any large undertaking such as your geography project needs a goodly supply of dog's bodies. Be sure to have a ready stock of snacks, sandwiches and stimulants provided by your servants. Walk away from the television, but feel free to plug in your head-phones.

Janet Keeble (dog's body)

You can believe this – I didn't get to where I am now without action planning and sticking to deadlines. Don't over stretch yourselves, set your own agenda, keep to a decent timetable, and have some fun along the way. Even I was young once.

Tony Thomas (Chief Executive of the Field Studies Council)

Appendix

The country code

Make no unnecessary noise

Protect wildlife, plants and trees

Guard against all risks of fire

Keep to public paths across farmland

Keep your dog on a lead under close control!

Leave livestock, crops and machinery well alone

Avoid damaging fences, hedges and walls

Take all your litter home

Respect the life of the countryside

Fasten all gates

Specification matrix

A summary table showing selected topics/units relevant to geographical fieldwork across the main awarding bodies.

Only those themes relevant to coursework have been included, e.g. Development Studies are absent AS: lower VI (year 12), A2: upper VI (year 13) Entries in red are optional units	Awarding body/examining board						
	AQA A	AQA B	OCR A	OCR B	Edexcel A	Edexcel B	WJEC
Beach and coastal surveys (including management)	A2	AS	A2	AS	AS	AS	A2
Channel surveys (including hydrology)	AS	AS	A2	AS	AS	AS	AS
Ecosystems and succession (including management)	AS	A2	AS	AS	A2	A2	AS
Farming surveys	AS		A2			AS	
Glacial processes and landforms		AS	A2	A2	A2	AS	A2
Gradient/slope surveys (including weathering)			AS	AS	AS		A2
Land-use conflicts		AS	A2	A2		A2	A2
Leisure/recreational issues		A2	A2	A2		AS/A2	AS
Microclimate investigations		AS		A2		AS	A2
Pollution (air, noise and water)		A2				AS/A2	
Rural enquiries (including rural-urban fringe)	AS	AS	AS	AS	AS	AS	AS
Soil surveys	AS	A2	AS		A2		AS
Urban enquiries (land use and zonation)	AS	AS	AS	AS	A2	AS	AS
Individual investigation	A2	A2	AS	AS/A2	AS	AS	A2
Percentage of total A-level	20	15	15	15.7	20	16.7	16.7
Maximum word length	4000	4000	2500	2500	3000	2500	3500
Groupwork suggested?	✔	✔			✔	✔	✔

Note: It is possible to avoid a full length personal enquiry by opting for an alternative written exam on fieldwork skills (AQA A & B, OCR A and Edexcel A), but some of these include a 1000 word fieldwork report. (The above information is accurate at time of publication but may be subject to change.) For changes to the WJEC specification, please refer to the WJEC website (http://www.wjec.co.uk/).

Key to dating houses Only typical examples from each period are shown (approximate time periods used).

1. Tudor, timber framed (pre-1700)

2. Georgian, terraced (1700-1830s)

3. Victorian, terraced (1837-1901)

4. Edwardian, villas (1902-1919)

5. Inter-war council, semi-detached (1920-1945)

6. Inter-war private, semi-detached (1920-1945)

7. Post-war private, semi-detached (1946-1970)

8. Post-war residential blocks/ maisonnettes (1946-1970)

9. Post-war tower blocks (1946-1970)

10. Modern detached (post-1970)

11. Modern semi-detached starter homes (post-1970)

12. Modern 'sheltered' bungalows (post-1970)

Simplified land utilisation key

Arable – cereals

Arable – market vegetables (including root crops)

Deciduous or mixed woodlands

Coniferous plantations

Grassland pasture

Market gardens, orchards, nurseries, allotments

Heath, moorland and rough grazing

Open space – parklands, greens, public gardens

Commercial and residential

Roads, car parks, airfields, port areas, etc.

Industrial land, including utilities

Quarries, mines and tips

Derelict and waste land

Water features, e.g. rivers, lakes, bogs, canals

Note: You can add detail to these 14 basic land use categories by adding letter or number codings to this key, e.g. IN: industrial crops (oil-seed rape), SA: set-aside land.

IN | SA

Urban land-use key

A: Residential
A1 Houses, bungalows and gardens
A2 Flats, apartments, multi-occupancy dwellings
A3 Tower blocks and deck flats
A4 Hotels, Guest houses
A5 Hostels
A6 Sheltered accommodation

B: Retail
B1 Food shops – supermarkets, greengrocers, bakers, butchers, health food/delicatessens, etc.
B2 Convenience shops – newsagents, chemists, post offices, video rentals, fast food outlets
B3 Comparison shops – footwear, clothing, mobile phones, sports, antiques, etc.
B4 Specialist shops – florists, photographic, jewellers, pets, gifts, books, off-licence's, music, etc.
B5 Household shops – hardware, furniture/carpets, kitchenware, fabrics, second hand
B6 Consumer durables – electrical goods (televisions, videos, white goods, etc.), computers
B7 Service shops – hairdressers, dry cleaners, travel agents, betting, shoe repairs, printers, garages
B8 Chain/department stores – Boots, Marks and Spencers, Woolworths, Debenhams, C&A, Wilkinsons, etc.
B9 Charity shops – Oxfam, Save the Children, Mind, etc.
B10 Vacant premises

C: Professional and commercial
C1 Banks and building societies
C2 Estate agents, surveyors
C3 Legal services – solicitors
C4 Financial – insurance services, accountants
C5 Health services – doctors, dentists, opticians, osteopaths, witch doctors, etc.
C6 Company offices
C7 Society offices, e.g. Unions
C8 Other services, e.g. multi-storey car parking
C9 Vacant commercial premises

D: Industrial
D1 Factories and manufacturing
D2 Warehousing – storage, distribution and yards
D3 Utilities – gas works, electrical sub-stations, telephone exchanges, sewage works, etc.
D4 Business parks – light manufacturing
D5 Disused/derelict premises and land

E: Public buildings
E1 Educational premises
E2 Places of worship
E3 Museum/library/art gallery
E4 Police, fire and ambulance
E5 Central and local government offices – town halls, job centres, benefit and housing offices
E6 Hospitals and clinics
E7 Tourist information centre
E8 Toilets
E9 Bus/rail stations, ports (air/sea)

F: Recreation and leisure
F1 Public houses, inns, bars, nightclubs
F2 Restaurants, cafés, snack bars
F3 Leisure centres and keep-fit palaces
F4 Social clubs and community halls
F5 Cinemas, theatres, concert halls
F6 Amusement arcades, bingo halls, etc.

G: Open space
G1 Public parks, greens and gardens
G2 Sports grounds, playing fields, golf courses
G3 Cemetery, crematoria
G4 Conservation site
G5 Car, coach, lorry parks (surface)
G6 Allotments
G7 Agricultural land
G8 Roads, strees, pavements, footpaths, etc.
G9 Unused/derelict site
G10 Development/construction site

Notes
- This urban land-use key is thorough but not exhaustive and sometimes it is not that easy to identify the dominant function at every site. Multi-activity functions, e.g. 'pound-stretcher' shops, may not fit conveniently into the key (they can be either B5 or B8).

- Further detail can be introduced by using a letter to represent the precise function, e.g. library: E3L, jewellers: B4J, sewage works: D3S.

- On some surveys it may help to identify key indicator activities, e.g. charity shops, vacant premises, comparison shops by over-shading, using diagonal lines.

- This land-use key does not match the official categories and codings used by town planners and developers.

Land capability classes

Class	General description	Typical land use
1	Low lying flat land, deep fertile soils (pH = 6-7), well drained loamy texture, few stones, light rainfall (<750mm/yr), e.g. East Anglian Fens	Cash crops and cereals
2	Lowland, shallow slopes (generally <5°), fairly deep soils (>50cm), reasonable drainage, slightly acidic, e.g. many parts of central and southern England	Cereals and mixed farming
3	Intermediate land with greater altitude and slopes (generally <12°), shallower less fertile soils (<50cm), some drainage problems, becoming acidic (pH = 5-6) and stony, e.g. south west England	Dairying and mixed farming
4	Higher and more exposed land, more strongly sloping (>12° in parts), shallow, acidic and stony soils (<30cm), poorly drained in parts (often needing improvements), e.g. mid Wales	Hill cattle and sheep
5	Exposed upland, some steep slopes (>20°) very thin and stony soils or thick peat, very acidic (pH = <4.5), poorly drained soils, high annual rainfall (>1200mm), e.g. Pennines	Rough grazing of sheep at best Coniferous plantations

Relative humidity tables (for whirling psychrometer)

Dry Bulb reading (°C)

Dry bulb temperature

Difference (°C)	6	7	8	9	10	11	12	13	14	15	16	17	18	19	20	21	22	23	24
0.5	93	93	94	94	94	94	94	95	95	95	95	95	95	95	96	96	96	96	96
1.0	86	87	87	88	88	88	89	89	90	90	90	90	91	91	91	91	92	92	92
1.5	79	80	81	82	82	83	83	84	84	85	85	86	86	86	87	87	88	88	88
2.0	73	74	75	76	76	77	78	79	79	80	81	81	82	82	83	83	83	84	84
2.5	66	67	69	70	71	72	73	74	74	75	76	77	77	78	78	79	80	80	80
3.0	60	61	63	64	65	66	68	69	70	71	71	72	73	74	75	76	76	77	77
3.5	53	55	57	58	60	61	62	64	65	66	67	68	69	70	70	71	72	72	73
4.0	47	49	51	53	54	56	57	59	60	61	63	64	65	65	66	67	68	69	69
4.5	41	43	45	47	49	51	53	54	56	58	58	59	61	62	63	64	64	65	66

Difference in temperature (= dry bulb - wet bulb)

Use this table to calculate **percentage** relative humidity. For example, if the dry bulb thermometer registers 15°C and the wet bulb 12.5°C, the difference is 2.5°C. The relative humidity is therefore 75%.

Random numbers extract (arranged in two-digit pairings)

Row No.	Random numbers						
1	20 17	42 48	23 17	59 66	38 61	02 10	86 10
2	74 49	04 49	03 04	10 33	53 70	11 54	48 63
3	94 70	49 31	38 67	23 42	29 65	40 88	78 71
4	22 15	78 15	69 84	32 52	32 54	15 12	54 02
5	93 29	12 18	27 30	30 55	91 87	50 57	58 51
6	71 58	45 43	72 69	18 67	32 57	29 16	02 58
7	82 14	64 47	40 74	53 03	75 40	28 63	53 36
8	41 01	53 67	41 78	84 29	26 34	42 19	82 13
9	30 63	22 27	28 69	36 23	99 52	29 03	87 28
10	73 09	03 54	20 02	55 49	48 46	75 42	62 63
11	66 41	48 46	17 24	82 51	86 86	53 66	95 57
12	70 10	21 02	71 89	14 80	64 32	58 17	35 65
13	59 55	94 44	77 90	01 99	79 48	28 61	93 87
14	75 81	42 45	69 28	23 90	46 24	32 97	64 41
15	72 22	05 84	39 89	57 73	84 86	57 76	79 08
16	47 14	97 61	57 30	93 88	12 88	58 15	75 17
17	98 75	58 14	05 05	16 72	57 34	20 46	91 04
18	64 71	77 50	51 00	61 02	60 51	13 61	34 33
19	43 12	46 66	40 56	39 77	75 32	80 30	22 90
20	59 70	15 36	67 19	12 59	39 42	35 24	69 86

Instructions

- The two-digit pairings of random numbers are arranged so that they can be easily used as 4-figure co-ordinates, e.g. 20 17.

- Start at any point, but you should then read off in consistent directions, e.g. in row 20 start with 59 70, and then read across (15 36, etc.) or upwards (43 12, etc.) or diagonally (46 66, etc.).

- Numbers can also be read singly, in pairs or multiples of three or four.

Invertebrate indicators of pollution

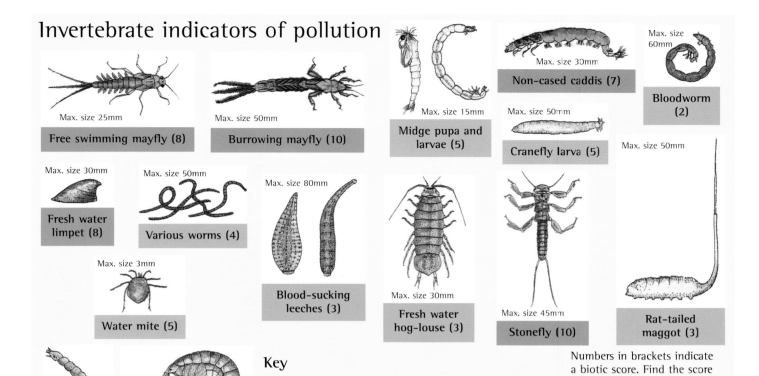

Max. size 25mm
Free swimming mayfly (8)

Max. size 50mm
Burrowing mayfly (10)

Max. size 15mm
Midge pupa and larvae (5)

Max. size 30mm
Non-cased caddis (7)

Max. size 50mm
Cranefly larva (5)

Max. size 60mm
Bloodworm (2)

Max. size 30mm
Fresh water limpet (8)

Max. size 50mm
Various worms (4)

Max. size 80mm
Blood-sucking leeches (3)

Max. size 30mm
Fresh water hog-louse (3)

Max. size 45mm
Stonefly (10)

Max. size 50mm
Rat-tailed maggot (3)

Max. size 3mm
Water mite (5)

Max. size 10mm
Black fly larvae (5)

Max. size 25mm
Fresh-water shrimp (6)

Key

High oxygen demanders = cleaner water

Moderate oxygen demanders

Low oxygen tolerators = polluted water

Numbers in brackets indicate a biotic score. Find the score for each animal in your sample, total the scores, and divide by the sample number to give a mean value for each sample site. The higher the mean, the cleaner the water.

Lichens key

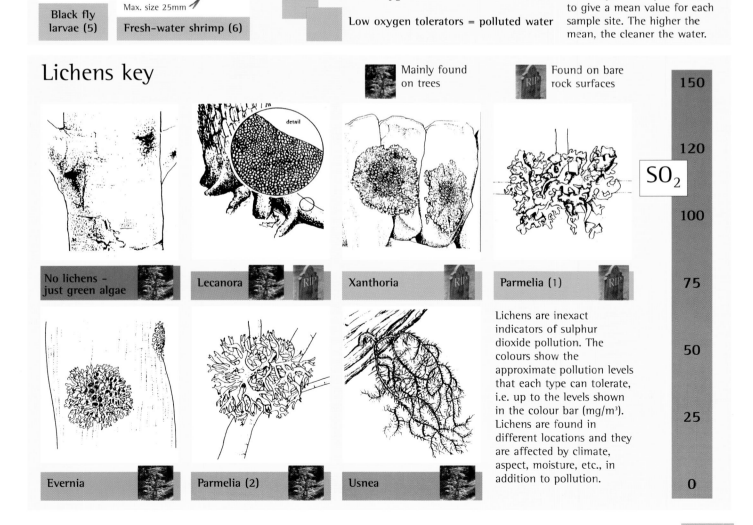

Mainly found on trees

Found on bare rock surfaces

No lichens – just green algae

Lecanora

Xanthoria

Parmelia (1)

Evernia

Parmelia (2)

Usnea

SO₂ bar: 150, 120, 100, 75, 50, 25, 0

SO$_2$

Lichens are inexact indicators of sulphur dioxide pollution. The colours show the approximate pollution levels that each type can tolerate, i.e. up to the levels shown in the colour bar (mg/m³). Lichens are found in different locations and they are affected by climate, aspect, moisture, etc., in addition to pollution.

Glossary

Glossary of terms which appear in **bold**.

Accuracy. The reliability or correctness of data/information, e.g. Big Ben is an accurate clock.

Acid rain. The additional acidification of water droplets in the atmosphere due to a build-up of SO_2 (pH <5.0).

Aesthetic. The sensory quality of appreciating visual landscapes.

Amenities. Community facilities which may cater for social, cultural, recreational and/or leisure needs.

Annotate. To add explanatory comments or notes with linking arrows around a map or diagram.

Antecedent. The previous state of a physical system, e.g. saturated soils.

Aspect. The compass direction in which a feature, e.g. a slope, faces.

Assimilation (zone of). An urban area or zone which is experiencing growth and regeneration (see Figure 5 in Urban Enquiries).

Audit. This is a detailed assessment of an existing operation, for example, schools may carry out audits where the environmental cost of heating, lighting, cooking, water usage, are evaluated.

Bedding plane. A surface which marks the interruption or change in the depositional history of sedimentary rocks.

Biogeochemicals. The movement, at various scales, of mineral and compounds through the ecosystem.

Biosphere. The living layer on Earth - comprising the lithosphere (rock), the hydrosphere (water) and the atmosphere (air).

Boy racers. Typically young males (aged between 17 and 27) who seem unaware of any other road users or pedestrians and who drive in a fast, erratic and reckless manner particularly on narrow country lanes.

Braiding. A process occurring in rivers as a response to marked variations in seasonal discharge.

Brashing. A technique used by managers of commercial woodland whereby small branches are removed from young trees.

Break in slope. A significant change in the angle of a slope, for example, hard rocks which cause waterfalls or rapids.

Brownfield site. An old industrial or derelict site (within an urban area) which has been redeveloped or is ripe for development.

Calibration. A process whereby instrument readings or scales are corrected with a known standard so they are made accurate. For example, altimeters need to be calibrated according to current air pressure.

Catchment area. The whole area over which a particular feature exerts an influence (applies to rivers, shops, schools, etc.)

Catena. A sequence of soils down a slope where each soil type reflects the environmental conditions.

Census. Household data collected every ten years by the government on the size and nature of the UK's population.

Citizenship. Being an active and responsible member of a social/community group.

Competence. The diameter of the largest pebble/boulder that a river can transport with a given velocity or energy.

Control group. This is a group used for comparative purposes when analytical studies take place on an experimental group.

Coppicing. Periodic cutting, or pruning, of a tree which results in new growth so that the tree can be 'harvested' every few years. The cut branches are used for making, e.g. fence posts or charcoal.

Correlation. The degree of relationship between two or more variables or data sets, e.g. altitude and temperature.

Cost-benefit analysis. A type of audit – an approach used by planners to assess whether the financial costs of a scheme will be more than covered by the resulting benefits. Typically undertaken for major construction schemes.

Cosy spots. Places where people like you tend to gather, as they are familiar, contained and possibly safe from intrusion, for example, school bike sheds and the sixth-form social area.

Criteria. These are statements or descriptors which are useful in measuring or valuing whatever is under investigation, e.g. development criteria include - GNP per head, birth/death rates, literacy rates.

Delimit. To define a spatial boundary, e.g. a watershed delimits a river's drainage basin.

Deprivation. A reduced quality of life due to poor health, low income, lack of education and/or lack of employment opportunities.

Desire line. A line that represents the movement of people from, for example, their home or a car park, to another location.

Discard (zone of). An urban area which is experiencing neglect or decay and showing signs of becoming run-down (see Figure 5 in Urban Enquiries).

Distribution. The spread pattern on a map of a particular feature, e.g. comparison shops tend to be clustered.

Diurnal. Fluctuations in a variable over the 24hr period in a day, particularly used with temperature.

Diversity. A measure of the types or variety of species present, e.g. traditional hay meadows have a high diversity.

Dominancy. The most competitive, successful and prevalent species in a given environment, e.g. on moorlands heather is often dominant.

Ecosystem. A self-sustaining community (e.g. a forest or pond) of living organisms (called the biotic component) and their non-living surroundings (the abiotic component, e.g. bedrock, climate).

Electoral Register. A street-by-street record of residents listed by house number.

Empathy. The ability to relate to and understand other peoples' feelings and attitudes.

Eutrophication. The nutrient enrichment of water in rivers and lakes by the accumulation of soluble residues, e.g. nitrates and phosphates encourage algal blooms in summer, particularly where the circulation is restricted.

Factor. A number or item which forms part of a whole thing or process, e.g. many factors affect stream discharge.

Feasible. How realistic, practical or sensible a particular option is.

Field headlands. The conservation margin left around arable fields in an attempt to encourage wildlife diversity (typically 5m wide).

Fieldwork fatigue. The onset of boredom or exhaustion due to over exposure to coursework or fieldwork. Common symptoms include loss of energy and interest, glazed eyeballs and trembling of the extremities.

Formal activities. Organised group recreational activities, e.g. sporting teams, ramblers, fox hunting.

Function. The main purpose for which a piece of land or a building is utilised, e.g. car park, retail shops.

Gentrification. The process of upgrading properties in, e.g. inner cities, market towns and villages, by affluent incomers.

Globalisation. The breaking down of national barriers through the global trading of goods, services and communications.

Green belt. A countryside zone intended to restrain the expansion of a conurbation through planning control.

Greenfield site. Agricultural land that has been designated for development for industrial, commercial or urban uses.

Hectare. A square area 100m x 100m (similar in size to a large football pitch). 100 hectares = 1km^2.

Hierarchy. An ordering of settlements, shops, roads, etc., in order of importance or scale, Pubs, for example, are of low order.

Honeypot site. A beauty spot or leisure facility which attracts large numbers of visitors and may suffer from over-use.

Hotspots. Sites of extreme activity, e.g. volcanic eruptions, high pedestrian densities.

Humidity (relative). The actual water vapour content of air, in comparison to the amount that the air could hold at a given pressure and temperature. This is measured as a percentage, e.g. the rainforests are at nearly 100%.

Hydrological. Anything related to the movement or transfer of water, e.g. interception, throughflow, gutters/drains.

Hypothesis. A statement of a logical expectation or 'hunch' which can be tested through data collection. The outcome can be either accepted, rejected or found to be inconclusive.

Index. A figure resulting from calculations involving ratios, divisions, percentages or rankings which may not have a unit of measure, e.g. hydraulic radius. (It is also an alphabetical sorting of items.)

Indicator species. A plant or animal which is representative of a particular set of environmental conditions, e.g. mayfly nymphs indicate clean water, whilst sewage fungus indicates gross organic pollution.

Individualisation. The processes whereby council tenants buy up their homes and personalise them with, for example, the installation of distinctive front doors.

Isolines/isopleths. Imaginary lines joining points of equal value, e.g. contours, isobars, isochrones, isotherms.

Key Settlement. Designated small towns or villages where economic and/or housing growth is encouraged by the local authority.

Large-scale. A large-scale map covers only a small area but reveals a lot of detail, e.g. 1:1250 is large-scale.

Long profile. A cross-section of a feature from beginning to end, e.g. a river system from source to mouth.

Matrix. A tabulation in which the rows 'interact' with the columns to give a table of cells. These are often used to make judgements about the scale of impacts to do with activities and developments.

Mean. The mathematical average of a data set or series of numbers.

Micro/macro. A description of scale, i.e. micro = very small (a playground), macro = very large (a city).

Modal (mode). The value or group that occurs most frequently in a data set.

Morphology. The study of the shape or form of a geographical feature, e.g. a town or coastline.

NIMBY (not in my back-yard). An attitude towards a particular proposal that may be for the common good, but which people are reluctant to have built on their doorstep, e.g. certain types of hostel.

Objective. Information gathering which is unbiased (not influenced by personal likes or dislikes).

Organic/inorganic pollution. Organic pollutants tend to be biodegradable, e.g. sewage, milk, whilst inorganic pollutants, e.g. lead, mercury, have a much longer residence time in the environment. The latter constitute a greater health risk, particularly as they can be accumulated and transferred through food chains.

Ozone (low level). A photochemical reaction at or near ground level which causes visual, respiratory and plant pollution.

Peer group. A group of friends/colleagues who are in the same boat as you.

pH. A measure of the acidity or alkalinity of soil or water. It is based upon a logarithmic scale from 1-14.

Pilot survey. A preliminary visit to a fieldwork site/testing of a questionnaire to assess the feasibility of a proposed survey.

Plagiarism. A long word for cheating through the act of copying (see the X-Files).

PLVI (peak land value intersection). Places in the core area of the central business district where the land values are highest.

Point-bars. Gently sloping gravel banks of deposited material found on the inside of river meanders.

Pollution. Human activities which lead to the contamination or altering of the natural environment. This occurs where the concentration of waste products exceeds the rate of dispersal by natural systems, e.g. acid rain.

Pools and riffles. These are changing energy environments within a section of river channel. Energy is conserved in the deeper pools (outside of meanders) and dissipated in the shallower riffles (straighter sections).

Population pyramid. A horizontal bar graph which represents the age and gender structure of a population.

ppm (parts per million). Usually very small quantities, equivalent to 1mg per litre, i.e. 10ppm = 0.00001.

Precision. The number of decimal places that you might give a realistic answer to, e.g. 2.12 is more precise than 2.1.

Prediction/predictive. A statement or idea concerning the likely future events or outcomes.

Provenance. Evidence which indicates the place of origin of something, e.g. registration plates on cars.

Qualitative. Fieldwork data based on subjective observations and descriptions, e.g. field sketches.

Quantitative. Where objective numerical data is measured and collected during fieldwork, e.g. river discharge.

Rank order. Numbers or items placed in order from the largest to the smallest.

Relationship. A term used to describe whether two items have a link or connection, e.g. drugs and street crime.

Render. A computer modelling technique used to produce a three-dimensional image of a digitised landscape.

Respondent. The person to whom you, as interviewer, direct your interview or questionnaire.

Segregation. The separation of differing residential and functional zones by physical features, socio-economic characteristics or by deliberate planning, e.g. cycle-tracks should be segregated from roads.

Significance. The level at which a statistical relationship or impact/process becomes meaningful and convincing.

Signposting. Advanced GCE specifications highlight opportunities for key skills to be achieved and evidenced.

Sinuosity. A term describing the degree of curvature of a river channel, i.e. meanders have a sinuous form.

Skill audit. A detailed self-assessment of an individual's competencies. Examples include interpersonal skills, practical, numeric, artistic, graphical, problem solving and communication skills.

Small-scale. A small-scale map covers a large area but only shows basic information, e.g. world maps, road atlases.

Socio-economic. Describes all aspects of a population to do with its demography, culture, income, health, etc.

Spatial. An adjective referring to area or space, i.e. geography is a spatial subject.

Specification. A structure of work that you follow and will be assessed upon – the new term for syllabus.

Sphere of influence. An area around a settlement or function which is served by this feature, e.g. a town, an airport, a corner shop.

SSSI (site of special scientific interest). Sites of significant ecological or geological value which carry a measure of protection from change. There are several thousand of these in the UK.

Stand. Vegetation which is all the same, usually planted at the same time, e.g. a stand of conifers.

Stereotypical. Views and attitudes which conform to an unjustifiably fixed and biased impression, e.g. women are obsessed with shopping, men are incapable of changing a toilet roll.

Stevenson Screen. A white, wooden slatted box located in open space, in which weather recording instruments are kept.

Stream order. The ranking of streams according to their place in the hierarchy of a tributary network.

Succession. The gradual and predictable change in plant and animal species over time. The process starts with the colonisation of a barren area (pioneer community) and proceeds through seral stages to a mature and stable climax community.

Sustainability. A complex idea in which development is managed to minimise environmental degradation so that both today's needs and those of future generations are assured.

Talking heads. A technique in which a head and a speech bubble are employed to capture people's views, attitudes and feelings.

Temporal. An adjective referring to time. Rivers for example, will have 'temporal' variations in their seasonal discharge patterns.

Tenure. The legal basis upon which property is occupied, e.g. owner-occupier, local authority tenant.

Thinning. The selective removal of immature trees in a woodland to create space for healthier growth.

Threshold (population). The minimum population required to support and sustain a particular product or service.

Topography. A physical description of the shape of the landscape, e.g. flat, undulating, hilly, mountainous.

Transect. A line used in fieldwork for gaining a representative sample, e.g. along a road, hedge.

Transferable skills. These are competencies or proficiencies that you might acquire in one subject, e.g. geography, and may be able to use in other situations, e.g. other examinable subjects, part-time employment, nightclubs.

Trend. The compass orientation of geographical features, e.g. mountains, drumlins, footpaths.

Turbidity. A disturbance to either the smooth flow or clarity of a river.

Variable. A changing quantity that can have different values depending upon circumstances, for example, if you walk up Everest the following variables will change - temperature, wind speed, air pressure, mood, etc.

Vermin. Used to describe certain animals or people which are damaging to the quality of life, e.g. rats.

Weathering. The physical/chemical breakdown and decomposition of mineral matter (rocks) in their original position.

Weighting. A qualitative device to emphasise the greater importance or significance of certain factors/criteria by increasing the scored value (see Figure 1 in Environmental Impact Assessment).

Wildscape. An area which may be wild, rugged, and deserted, showing minimal impact by people, e.g. Antarctica, Gobi Desert, parts of Scotland.

Contacts

Awarding bodies

AQA
Comprising AEB and NEAB. Contact: (AEB address) Stag House, Guildford, Surrey GU2 5XJ. Tel: 01483 506 506; fax: 01483 300 152; e-mail: geo@neab.ac.uk or geog@aeb.org.uk Website: http://www.aqa.org.uk (includes both AEB and NEAB specifications)

Edexcel Foundation
Incorporates London (16-19) and BTEC. Contact: Stewart House, 32 Russell Square, London WC1B 5DN. Tel: 0870 240 9800; fax: 020 7758 6960; e-mail: enquiries@edexcel.org.uk Website: http://www.edexcel.org.uk

OCR
Syndicate of Oxford and Cambridge awarding bodies. Contact: 1 Regent Street, Cambridge CB2 1GG. Tel: 01223 553998; fax: 01223 552627; e-mail: helpdesk@ocr.org.uk Website: http://www.ocr.org.uk

Welsh Joint Education Council
245 Western Avenue, Cardiff CF5 2YX. Tel: 029 2026 5000; fax: 029 2057 5894 Website: http://www.wjec.co.uk/

Environment and conservation

Countryside Council for Wales
Publish descriptions of nature reserves and other information. Contact: Plas Penrhos, Ffordd Penrhos, Bangor, Gwynedd LL57 2LP. Tel: 01248 385500 Website: http://www.ccw.gov.uk

English Nature
Publish descriptions of nature reserves and other information. Contact: Northminster House, Peterborough PE1 1UA. Tel: 01733 455000; fax: 01733 568834 Website: http://www.english-nature.org.uk

Field Studies Council
Run field courses from 15 centres in England and Wales. Also produces publications and leaflets. Contact: Montford Bridge, Shrewsbury, Shropshire SY4 1HW. Tel: 01743 852 100; fax: 01743 852 101; e-mail: enquiries@field-studies-council.org Website: http://www.field-studies-council.org

National Parks
Information on all the UK national park websites can be accessed through: http://www.nationalparks.org.uk

Scottish Natural Heritage
Publish descriptions of nature reserves and other information. Contact: 12 Hope Terrace, Edinburgh EH9 2AS. Tel: 0131 447 4784; e-mail: enquiries@snh.gov.uk Website: http://www.snh.org.uk

The Wildlife Trusts
A conservation organisation, which may have biological records of wildlife sites. See website for details of local offices. Contact: The Kiln, Waterside, Mather Road, Newark NG24 1WT. Tel: 0870 036 7711; fax: 0870 036 0101; e-mail: info@wildlife-trusts.cix.co.uk Website: http://www.wildlifetrusts.org

Equipment

Dryden Aquaculture
Suppliers of Ozone detector cards. Contact: Butlerfield Industrial Estate, Bonnyrigg, Edinburgh EH19 3JQ. Tel: 01875 822222 Website: http://www.drydenaqua.com

Griffin and George
Major UK suppliers of scientific equipment for fieldwork. Contact: Bishop Meadow Road, Loughborough LE11 0RG. Tel: 01509 233344; fax: 01509 231893; e-mail: griffin@fisher.co.uk Website: http://www.griffinandgeorge.co.uk

Merck Ltd
Suppliers of chemicals and water and 'BDH' soil testing kits. Contact: Merck House, Broom Road, Poole BH12 1TD. Tel: 01202 669700; fax: 01202 665599; e-mail: davidhall@merck-ltd.co.uk Website: http://www.merck-ltd.co.uk

Owens and Boys Field Study Products
Manufacturers of hydro-prop flow meters. Contact: 16 St Winifreds Road, Cefn Glas, Bridgend CF31 4PL. Tel: (M-F 5-9pm) 01656 660311; fax: 01656 646952; e-mail: dowens@netcomuk.co.uk

Philip Harris
Major equipment suppliers to schools and colleges. Contact: Philip Harris Education, Findel House, Excelsior Road, Ashby Park, Ashby de la Zouch, Leicestershire LE65 1NG. Tel: 0845 120 4520; fax: 01530 419 492; e-mail: tech@education.philipharris.co.uk Website: http://www.philipharris.co.uk/

Secondary data and publications

While most of the organisations on this page publish resources which you may be able to use during your fieldwork, you can contact the following for specific information.

The Geological Society
Holds records of over 200 000 geological sites in UK. Contact: Burlington House, Piccadilly, London W1J 0BG. Tel: 020 7434 9944; fax: 020 7439 8975; e-mail: enquiries@geolsoc.org.uk Website: http://www.geolsoc.org.uk

Geographical Association
Produces geography resources and advice for students and teachers. Contact: 160 Solly Street, Sheffield S1 4BF. Tel: 0114 296 0088; fax: 0114 296 7176; e-mail: ga@geography.org.uk Website: http://www.geography.org.uk

Maps and plans

- Downloadable maps are available at websites: http://www.mapquest.com and http://www.ordsvy.gov.uk

Goad Map Shop
Suppliers of town centre land-use maps. Contact: 8-12 Salisbury Square, Old Hatfield, Herts AL9 5BJ. Tel: 01707 636900; fax: 01707 636907

National Map Centre
Ordnance Survey map agents. Contact: 22 Caxton Street, London SW1H 0QH. Tel: 020 7263 2444; fax: 020 7272 3309; e-mail: info@mapsworld.com Website: http://www.mapsworld.com

Ordnance Survey
Will provide details of your local OS map supplier. Contact: Romsey Road, Southampton, SO16 4GU. Tel: 023 8079 2912; fax: 023 8079 2615; e-mail: customerservices@ordsvy.gov.uk Website: http://www.ordsvy.gov.uk

Royal Geographical Society
Map room and library in central London. Contact: 1 Kensington Gore, London SW7 2AR. Tel: 020 7591 3000; fax: 020 7591 3001; e-mail: info@rgs.org Website: http://www.rgs.org

Statistics and other information

- Air quality information and statistics for the UK is available at: http://www.airquality.co.uk
- The BBC website includes information on pollen counts: http://www.bbc.co.uk/weather/pollen/index.shtml
- Ceefax, pages 410-417, and Teletext, page 106, also include weather data.

Department of Transport and the Regions
The DETR website holds data on transport and regional development: Website: http://www.detr.gov.uk

Environment Agency
Monitors air and water quality. Local offices listed in telephone directory. Contact: Public Register: King's Meadow House, King's Meadow Road, Reading RG1 8DQ. E-mail: paul.williams@environment-agency.gov.uk Website: http://www.environment-agency.gov.uk

European Blue Flag
Website includes information on the basic EU standards for tourist beaches: Website: http://www.blueflag.org.uk

Highways Agency
May hold traffic count data and road plans. Contact: St Christopher House, Southwark Street, London SE1 0TE. Tel: 0345 504030; fax: 020 7921 4899; e-mail: ha_info@highways.gsi.gov.uk Website: http://www.highways.gov.uk

Meteorological Office
Provide meteorological and climate data for UK. Contact: Education Services, Room S2/11, Sutton House, London Road, Bracknell, Berkshire RG12 2SU. Tel: 0845 300 0300; fax: 0845 300 1300; e-mail: dchardy@meto.gov.uk Website: http://www.met-office.gov.uk

Office for National Statistics
Holds a large range of demographic data. Contact: 1 Drummond Gate, London SW1V 2QQ. Tel: 020 7533 5249; e-mail: info@ons.gov.uk Website: http://www.ons.gov.uk

Tidy Britain Group
Website includes information on the 'Seaside Award for Beaches': Website: http://www.tidybritain.org.uk

Index